GREEN FIVE

Charles E. Cordell

Events described herein are based on actual wartime experiences of the author. Names and places have been changed to protect the privacy of the participants.

E.P. LAY & ASSOCIATES

ISBN: 0-9619184-1-1

W0010679

Contents

Foreword

This is a World War II flying story, different from most. It is about a 23-year old second lieutenant of the U.S. Marines, freshly minted as a Naval Aviator, a fighter pilot in the then-new cranked-wing Corsair. He was to serve his country for three years, yet never to hear a shot fired in anger.

Virtually all other books about wartime naval aviation feature the combat aspects of that lethal trade. Readers have been injected into chaotic flight deck scenes of carriers launching and recovering fighters, dive bombers, and torpedo planes. We have tingled to tales of airborne intercepts in cloud-dappled skies, of yammering machine guns and the reek of cordite, of skies full of flamers and seas ripped by splashers, and of the mass tragedies of sinking, burning capital ships.

This tale shows the other side of the coin, beginning with 2nd Lt. Cordell's experiences as a flight trainee, from the very beginning, working up to his technical education to participate in those swirling slugging matches in the vast skies of the Pacific. Then came his orders to the U.S. Navy Ferry Command. Rather than turning his guns on the enemy, he was fated to reposition naval aircraft from one part of the country to another — frequently from the East Coast to the West. It was, at first, a devastating blow to his morale, but he was to learn that he was also making a valuable contribution to the war effort.

Most of us have overlooked the issue of how those single-engine aircraft, once they were rolled out of the factory and production flight-tested, reached points of embarkation to sea transportation to the combat areas. This was the primary function of the Ferry Command.

And this is the story of one of its pilots, including how the assignment and experiences were to affect him for the rest of his life.

Frank Kingston Smith
Ocean City, New Jersey

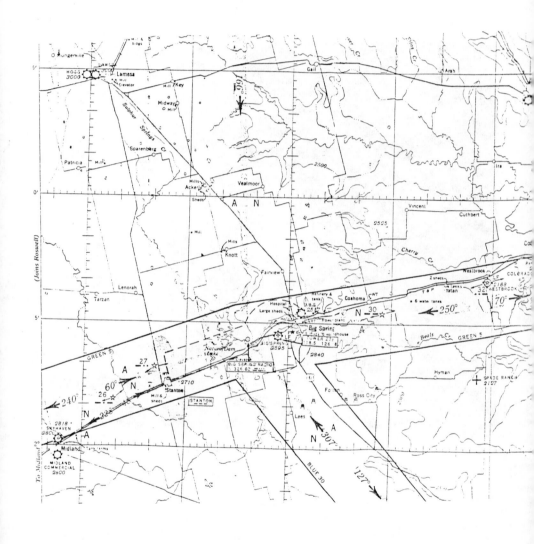

Learning the trade

One of the 50-caliber slugs from my Corsair's six machine guns apparently cut the tow cable about ten yards ahead of the target, a long, rectangular piece of quarter-inch mesh hardware cloth about three feet by twenty-five feet. It seemed to stop right in front of me as I approached from a "high side gunnery run" at about 300 knots. One does not think in such situations — there is not time — one simply reacts.

Instinctively, I shoved the control stick forward in an attempt to go under the target. This move was almost successful — but not quite. The tow cable lashed across the right wing about three feet inboard from its tip, slicing through the heavy-gauge aluminum leading edge like a hot knife through butter. The tough wing spar stopped it from severing the wingtip, but as it rasped over the wing it stripped the fabric from a portion of the right aileron. (Corsairs were all metal except for the control surfaces, which were fabric-covered.) The whole incident took perhaps two seconds.

My altimeter read 7,400 feet above the Atlantic Ocean. We were about 150 miles east of Jacksonville, Florida, our usual aerial gunnery practice area. Although we were over the Gulf Stream, the water that April day in 1944 looked cold. Climbing back into my formation slowed the airplane down and I slid the hatch back preparatory to leaving what I thought to be a disabled fighter. As I was about to unplug the earphones, my wingman, Arthur, who had followed me down in the gunnery run, erupted into his microphone:

"Who's the chisel-headed idiot that shot the target off?"

His ire was kindled by the fact that each of us used bullets coated with different colored paint so we could see who got hits when the tow pilot dropped the target back at our base. Arthur

1

apparently felt he had several hits and, without the bullet holes in the target as proof, he would never know. He was understandably miffed.

I immediately keyed my microphone. "This is Cisco 2-1" (my flight code name). "I did. And that's not all — I ran into it."

Lt. (j.g.) James Flournoy, USN, our flight leader and instructor -- got on the horn. "This is Cisco 1-1. Are you okay, 2-1?"

"I'm fine, but this airplane doesn't look so good," I replied.

"How's it fly?" he wanted to know.

"Well, it feels okay, but it's got a chunk out of the right wing so maybe you'd better come over and take a look at it."

By then my six squadron mates had moved in alongside me. Mr. Flournoy[1] eased his Corsair under my right wing to check for any damage that I couldn't see and gave us his report:

"Well, you've got quite a slice out of the leading edge and a torn aileron, but everything underneath seems to be okay. Let's go home."

The tow plane had already headed back to our practice base at Palatka, an outlying auxiliary field used for gunnery practice crews, located about 18 miles south of Green Cove Springs, Florida, Naval Auxiliary Air Station, our home base. We tagged along behind him and circled while he dropped the remains of the cable.

---

[1] The title "Mister" applied to officers is peculiar to the Naval branch of the military. Whereas in the Army and Air Force, lieutenants are addressed and referred to as "Lieutenant," the Navy uses the term "Mister." This usage can also apply to Marine Corps junior officers. The practice can prove confusing to civilians.

2

Mr. Flournoy stayed right on my wing for the 45 minutes it took us to return to base and told me to land first. I rolled the wheels gingerly on the asphalt at about 10 knots above stalling speed since I didn't know how much aileron control I would have at normal landing airspeed. Easing the tail down, I slowed to taxi speed and turned off the runway toward the parking ramp. The entire line crew came over to have a look at my "combat damage" as soon as the propeller stopped.

"Pretty neat piece of sheet metal work there, sir. You must have been really moving," one of the ordnance men commented.

As my flight mates pulled onto the ramp, I dismounted and walked around to assess the damage myself. The sturdy spar had held but there was a nasty gash in it where the cable had slid by it razor-like as the slipstream took it over the wing and ripped the aileron. About half the fabric was gone on the latter's top surface.

The shop chief strolled over and took a brief look, then glanced at my worried expression, saying, "Don't sweat it, sir. We'll have it back on the line in the morning."

As we boarded the shuttle bus back to Green Cove Springs, Arthur put his hand on my shoulder and apologized for his remarks on the radio. As they were completely understandable (all of us wanted to see our scores from the colored bullets), I good-naturedly needled him, "Since when did you start getting hits from a high side run?"

The other members of the flight chimed in, "Yeah, you couldn't hit the side of a barn from a beam shot!" It was comforting to hear their attempts to relieve any guilt at having ruined their practice session. Most of us had been together since Pre-Flight School days the previous summer and knew one another rather well.

The reference to the difficulty of a "beam shot" was only too true for all of us. Although affording maximum safety for the fighter pilot, "high side gunnery runs" required expert speed control and judgment of time and distance to be effective. With sufficient practice, however, a single division of fighters (four planes) could devastate a whole squadron of bombers enroute to their target with relative impunity.

Captain John Thach, USN, (nicknamed "Jimmy" Thach) had evolved the new fighter tactics from his personal experience in the South Pacific early in the war. By February 1944, when our flight had arrived fresh from graduation at Corpus Christi, Texas, as second lieutenants in the Marines, we already had received considerable instruction in the new "Thach tactics" in SNJ advanced trainers. In operational training at Green Cove Springs, we were merely honing our skills at these deadly arts in the aircraft we were to use overseas, the Chance Vought F4U, "Corsair."

To practice gunnery runs, one of our flight group (eight planes) would tow the target banner, attached to a hook on the tail of his plane with a 1,000-foot cable, out to sea at 8,000 feet and at a speed of 160 knots, the usual cruising speed of typical enemy bombers. The rest of us in "Cisco flight" would pull alongside, slightly ahead and to the right of the tow plane, about a quarter of a mile away and 2,000 feet higher. We would then assume a right echelon formation from which we would peel off one by one and head toward and ahead of the target.

Since the throttle was not retarded as we slowly rolled 180 degrees to pass the target 90 degrees to its line of flight, we were able to get off a three- or four-second burst of machine gun fire while approaching from abeam (thus the nomenclature "a beam shot") at extremely high speed. Our new Mark III gun sight would show us when we were within range (when the target filled the sight), and we would lead the target much the same as shooting ducks on the wing from a blind. Our adversary, were we in actual combat, however, would have a very poor target because of our closing speed and our head-on abeam approach. The system was excellent and proved to be extremely effective in combat patrols in the Pacific.

The runs could be executed from either side as overhead, high side, flat side, and low side runs. Caution was necessary in using the overhead run, however, since recovery required several thousand feet of altitude and, if begun below 10,000 feet, one might take out his target but the resulting shortage of recovery altitude could automatically even the score.

My stint at Green Cove Springs for operational training began three years previously when I was in college at Riverside, California. The school had been designated as one of the centers for the Government's new Civilian Pilot Training Program (CPTP). I was one of those students who had acquired "Lindbergh fever" in 1927 at the tender age of five, when the whole country was made aware of its aviation future by the Lone Eagle's epic flight across the Atlantic. My affliction continued into the 1930s with model airplanes and an actual flight in a real airplane, a 1929 "Travelair," whose intrepid pilot/owner was providing rides for the local gentry from our neighbor's cow pasture for the outrageous sum of $3.00. This open-cockpit biplane ride, plus another in a Sikorsky cabin model amphibian at the Chicago World's Fair in 1933, made an aviation career for me a virtual certainty.

I applied for the aviation CPTP program immediately, and I was enrolled in the college's first "Aviation Class."

Our primary training planes were two-place, tandem-seated, metal and fabric high-wing Aeronca monoplanes boasting all of 65 horsepower and cruising at the not-very-blinding speed of 75 to 80 miles per hour. Against almost any headwind, a pilot could look down at a local highway and observe ground traffic easily outdistancing him. Even so, the feeling of utter freedom was there, unique to pilots and impossible to describe adequately to laymen.

5

All aviators revel in this exhilarating sensation every time the airplane's wheels leave the ground. Every pilot can recall in minute detail the first time this happened.

In my own case, my instructor and I had begun our flight about 7 a.m. since I had to adapt my flight training schedule to my college schedule; my first class was at 9 a.m. My logbook showed all of seven and one-half hours when we took off into the rubescent early morning sky. We spent the first half hour of the session doing air work, then returned to the airfield to shoot a few landings. After three acceptable landings, my technique unraveled. Immediately after its fourth contact with the runway, the little Aeronca demonstrated its propensity to leap violently back into the air if the wheels didn't touch the ground at the exact moment the wings quit flying.

Crestfallen, I offered lamely, "Looks like I'm bouncing a little this morning."

"Yeah, that's for sure," was my instructor's laconic reply from the other seat. "Pull over to the edge of the runway and let me out. Then you can bounce it yourself."

"You think I'm okay for it now?" I swallowed hard.

"We'll soon find out, won't we?" He said with a smile, as he unbuckled his seatbelt, opened the door, and got out.

"Do two or three more, then come on in," he said cheerfully. He grinned and gave me an encouraging thumbs-up gesture, then turned and walked toward the hangar.

I managed a feeble smile in return and nudged the throttle. The little four-cylinder Continental engine rolled us to the end of the runway, where I aimed the propeller hub down the 2,000-foot dirt strip and fed in the power.

The tail came up, about 40 mph, then suddenly there was that magic sound of flight – the airframe no longer rattled with the noise of a ground-bound vehicle. For the first time in my life, I was flying all by myself. The other seat, so recently occupied by my protective instructor, was empty!

Curiously, I felt no fear; it was as if I was in my element. We climbed straight ahead to 600 feet, then a right turn while climbing to 800 feet, turned right again down the back stretch – the downwind leg – cut the throttle opposite the touchdown point, and pulled on the carburetor heat to prevent ice from forming in the throat of the carburetor and closing down the fuel flow. When this occurs, the unwary pilot suddenly finds himself in command of a glider.

Turning to final approach at 50 mph, I eased the stick back and crossed the airport boundary at 45. The end of the runway passed beneath the wheels and the mains and tailwheel all touched the ground at the same time.

Miracle of miracles, no bounce! I did it! I took an airplane up into the air all by myself and managed to get it down again in one piece. That memory will live in my mind forever.

The next two landings were passable, although not as smooth as my first solo. I pulled into the ramp area, turned off the switch, and watched the propeller twitch to a stop. For a few seconds, I sat in the almost silent cockpit; the only sounds were gentle popping noises as the engine cooled. Then I opened the door, climbed out, and hiked to the hangar office, carrying my parachute pack. Before I entered the door, I turned and glanced back at the assemblage of wood, fabric, and metal that had sustained me in flight. There is something undeniably miraculous about any airplane.

My reverie was broken by shouts of congratulations from my colleagues who had arrived for the next flight period. I was grabbed rudely by the arms while my shirt tail was snatched from my trousers and summarily cut off, then tacked to the wall alongside others evidencing, with names and dates, the entry of former earthlings into the realm of solo flight. Somehow, I didn't mind the loss of the shirt.

My instructor, who had been observing the skylarking with a wry smile, stuck out his hand and said, "You'll do," and patted me on the back, indicating that I had, indeed, joined a unique fraternity. It was very satisfying.

After completing my CPTP training and being awarded my private pilot's license early in June 1941, I was graduated from junior college and returned to my native Tennessee, where I entered the local university in Chattanooga. There, I took the ground school portion of secondary CPTP with advanced flight training at Chattanooga's Lovell Field. This phase of my civilian pilot training included a thorough indoctrination into the intricacies of aerobatic flight in an open-cockpit biplane, the Waco UPF7.

This airplane was remarkably suited for aerobatics; it was powered by a 190-horsepower Jacobs radial engine and was short coupled, a loosely used engineering term that alludes to the relative distance from the center of gravity of an airplane to its tail section. Up to a point, the shorter this distance, the more maneuverable the aircraft.

The Waco designer had apparently achieved the ideal coupling distance, making it an excellent aerobatic airplane with sufficient power and aileron control to do loops, slow rolls, Immelmann turns, snap-rolls, hammerhead stalls, tail-slides, and Cuban eights. It was also built strongly to take anticipated student abuse, such as falling out of the top of a loop or spinning inverted from a vertical reverse, plus the usual hard landings. Landings are rated as perhaps the most exacting maneuver performed in flying because they are always made with the airplane approaching the ground so there is no margin for error at all. The wide and soft landing gear on the Waco was helpful in eliminating the skittishness inherent in all short-coupled airplanes; for which I was often most grateful.

My training in the Waco was interrupted only briefly by Pearl Harbor and the resulting entry of the United States into World War II. Our entire CPTP group was dispatched to Atlanta, Georgia, on December 8, 1941, where we obtained our wartime I.D. cards, without which, as civilians, we would have been unable to fly. We also learned that we were no longer to be known as a Civilian Pilot Training Program but rather War Training Service (WTS). Suddenly, the "fun and games" of properly executing loops, rolls, and vertical reverses took on a deadly new meaning — gunnery runs, dive bombing, and aerial dogfights in defense of our homeland. Therefore, it was with a new feeling of patriotic zeal that I began to polish my flying skills as we continued to the end of our course in secondary training and received our certificates of completion.

During my course of instruction at Chattanooga, I had taken a Civil Service job as a "junior historical aide" at Point Park, Lookout Mountain, Tennessee. My duties at this National Park site, 2,000 feet above Chattanooga and overlooking the picturesque Moccasin Bend of the Tennessee River, consisted of guiding and answering the questions of tourists visiting the Park. My colleagues there graciously allowed me to arrange my schedule so I could use my lunch period each day to go down the mountain, across town to the airport, fly an hour, and return. I became

9

quite adept at dodging Chattanooga traffic while munching a sandwich.

The six-month tour at the Park ended almost at the same time I completed my flight training at Lovell Field. Therefore, although I had become quite proficient at flying an airplane, I learned of a need for civilian electronics technicians at Ft. McPherson Army Base at Atlanta. Since I had been an amateur radio operator for over three years, I moved to Atlanta and accepted the job. While still a civilian I was thus contributing to the war effort both as a radio telegraph operator and as a maintenance technician.

By November 1942, the flying urge began to re-assert itself and I presented myself at the Naval Aviation Cadet Selection Board to join the Naval Reserve and enroll in the V-5 Aviation Cadet Program. I vividly recall the look of joy on the recruiting yeoman's face when I told him, "I'm twenty years old, have completed two years of college, have finished primary and secondary WTS, and am in excellent health." After completing the necessary forms and physical exam, he administered the oath of allegiance then and there on November 9, 1942, and I was assigned to Class 43CC U.S. Naval Reserve. I was to remain in a civilian status at the electronics job until the cadets in my class had also completed WTS. Thus, I was not called to active duty until April 7, 1943.

My orders to Pre-Flight School at Athens, Georgia, arrived via telegram at Hialeah, Florida, on the morning of April 1, 1943, while I was at the top of a sixty-foot antenna pole, stringing the wires for what was to be the first Loran navigation system. It was to be used to navigate the aerial route to Africa via South America and Ascension Island. I did not know this at the time. All I knew was that I was installing a rhombic antenna and that the shanks of the pole-climbing spurs were gouging into my legs, the sun was unbearably hot, the mosquitos were dining on my arms, and I had just dropped a pair of pliers on my foot. Therefore, when one of my co-workers came running across the field waving the telegram ordering me to active duty, it was with great relief I clipped the last bit of wire from the insulators and climbed down.

After returning to Atlanta, I boarded the bus with several of my fellow cadets for the trip to Pre-Flight School at Athens. My previous experience with any sort of military uniform and protocol had been limited to that of Second Class Boy Scout. I addressed the Naval officer in charge, an ensign, as "Lieutenant." The correction was swift and merciless.

"You will address me as 'Mister,' Cadet!" he roared. "A fact with which you should be familiar if you had read your indoctrination manual!"

My education in military courtesy had begun.

Pre-Flight School on the University of Georgia campus at Athens was just that: physical and academic learning leading to flight training, but no flying at all. Mastering (and questioning the necessity of) close order drill, boxing and wrestling, military history and courtesy (floors and walls would be known thenceforth as "decks and bulkheads") all seemed to be interminable delays before our next duty as cadets, preliminary flight training.

From Athens, my reindoctrination to flight the Navy way was begun in Olathe, Kansas, in a biplane known as the N2S Stearman Navy trainer. My re-entry into the realm of flight came easily because of my previous training, since the Stearman was quite similar to the Waco in its flight characteristics, although not as short-coupled and heavier on the controls, particularly the ailerons.

My introduction to night flight came during the hitch at Olathe. Since skill at maintaining an airplane in stable flight depends on continual optical reference to several points on the ground and especially to the horizon, the visual loss of such reference points when flying on a dark night creates problems with depth perception. Because this is a prerequisite for all landings, pilots approaching unlighted runways at night in a glide tend either (a) to level off too soon, which results in the airplane literally falling from a height of several feet to the runway; or (b) to fly it into the ground at a flat angle. Either event can be jarring to the airplane and/or its pilot.

During my training, I had discovered that a few pilots who already wore the Navy wings of gold had acquired them through the Navy's V-6 program. This was an operation through which those who had some flight experience before the war could move immediately into the rank of ensign, take a brief refresher course, and become a primary flight instructor. The shortage of instructors made this process necessary due to the exigencies of war. Most of these pilots were excellent and did commendable jobs.

Sometimes, however, there were those individuals who had been subjected to certain social pressures to join the Naval Flying Service. The V-6 program was enticing to such persons since the much longer and more difficult V-5 Cadet regimen did not offer the quick commission and flight status necessary to relieve peer group pressure.

Ensign Lightner, who was to introduce me to the niceties of night flights, was apparently one of those unfortunate individuals. Mr. Lightner's attitude indicated he was not enamored with flying in general and not with night flying in particular. He was terrified.

His sole comment to me as we boarded the Stearman was: "Just watch me, Cadet, and follow me through."

We took off into the gloom and headed for one of our outlying practice fields. These were nothing more than pieces of flat Kansas meadows that the Navy had leased from various farmers in the area for use by cadets in the endless landing practice so necessary in building complete mastery of the airplane. By day they served quite admirably for this purpose.

At night, however, they were merely additions to the black void of which everything below the barely discernible horizon was composed. The inky blackness was broken occasionally by the lights in farmhouses and by the small glow of the surrounding towns. And, mercifully, our home base was well lighted. So when − and if − we finished our ordeal of practice, we could find our sanctuary relatively easily.

The only amenities added to these practice fields as an accommodation for our nocturnal adventures was a series of small kerosene-filled flare pots of the type used to designate danger spots along highway construction sites. They were placed in rows so that their flickering flames roughly outlined the strip of sod on which we were supposed to practice.

Lightner found the field by following one of his colleagues, who took off from the main base shortly before we did. He entered the so-called traffic pattern around the dimly-outlined strip and, when opposite the touchdown point, closed the throttle and banked toward the runway.

As we came around on final approach, he raised the nose enough to slow the Stearman to approach speed and pointed it at the space between the beginning of the rows of lights. The airplane had no landing lights, of course, so making the necessary judgment as to when to flare for landing was dependent entirely on depth perception which, in the Stygian blackness, was almost nonexistent.

He didn't flare it at all. The left wheel hit first, followed closely by the right, with a "KER-BONG!"

The rugged fuselage of the sturdy trainer reverberated with the shock as Lightner shoved the throttle ahead and said, "Okay, Cadet. That's the way you do it. Take me back to the base; then come back here and practice some by yourself."

After his departure from the front seat, I taxied back out and took off from the well-lighted runway and headed in the general direction of the practice strip. Rejoining the circle of red and green navigation lights of the half-dozen or so planes in the traffic circle, I established a proper sequence for landing.

I had evolved a possible solution to the problem of when to flare for touchdown between the rows of lights. I would leave the power on slightly and maintain the airplane in almost a three-point attitude as it descended. Upon contacting the ground, I would close the throttle so the airplane would remain on the ground completely stalled.

It worked.

Not until the next day did I learn from some of my fellow cadets that this procedure is the approved one for use in unlighted fields with aircraft not equipped with landing lights.

After five or six more landings, I became passably skillful and even began to develop an affinity for night flight. The air was smooth and bumpless in the absence of the thermals so characteristic of daytime flight. With some reluctance I returned to the main base about 10 p.m.

Lightner saw me come in.

"Any problems, Cadet?" he asked.

I walked on into the office. "No, sir," I replied.

"Kinda fun after you have done a few, huh?" Lightner asked.

"Yes, sir," I said. I wanted to remind him that he should try it more often himself but, military discipline being what it was, I felt such a remark might not be in good taste, even to a V-6 instructor. I put my parachute away and went over to the barracks.

Upon completion of preliminary flight training at Olathe, wherein we learned to fly the "Navy way," my class of aviation cadets was then considered ready for the heavier, more sophisticated service-type training planes at either Corpus Christi, Texas, or Pensacola, Florida.

As usual, the rumors were flying as to which of us would go to Pensacola which, for some obscure reason, was presumed to be the more desirable of the two. Finally the orders were released. We were going to Corpus Christi.

Rumors circulated at Olathe had it on good authority that our transportation to Corpus Christi would be first-class Pullman accommodations.

In fact, the antiquated cars we boarded at Kansas City were at least 50 years old and not air conditioned. Since the temperature in August varied to extremes, the cars were sweltering during the day, and the chill of night prevented what sleep we might have achieved in the ancient upright seats. Therefore, when the word was passed that we would be treated to a sumptuous meal upon our arrival, the purveyor of such information was subjected to such retorts as:

"Yeah, yeah. We know. The sun's gonna come up in the west in the morning, too."

But it happened.

Our train was hours late. The last food we had eaten had been stale sandwiches washed down with warm soft drinks when the train stopped at Houston, so we were ready to take on some fuel, as it was then early evening.

The Navy's "intake" personnel were equal to the problem. We were marched immediately to the Mess Hall for a delicious and filling meal.

The food was outstanding and copious in quantity, so a glimmer of confidence in Navy promises began to return. In addition, wonder of wonders, we were told we could "stroll about the base" after our evening meal and get acquainted with our new surroundings.

We broke up into groups of two or three and walked down to the PBY training squadron area on the bay.

This awesome airplane didn't look as if it would float, much less fly. Its broad, flat wing with its ancient but trustworthy Clark-Y airfoil section was set atop a pylon mounted on the roof of a fuselage constructed like a combination tank and small yacht. A huge stabilizer, fin, and rudder had been added to the rear as if to prove it was an airplane.

The tiny windows of the cockpit were just forward of the wing pylon area. Although used only for scout patrol and air/sea rescue, it was armed with a machine gun turret in the nose and two more guns in plexiglass and metal blisters on each side aft of the wing pylon. No amount of soundproofing could deaden the earth-shattering bellow of the two big Pratt & Whitney radial engines mounted on the wings just outboard of the pylon. The tips of the huge three-bladed propellers were only inches from the roof of the cockpit. At takeoff power, the tip speed exceeded the speed of sound, so a characteristic of all PBY pilots was a proclivity to say "Huh?" to every initial conversation.

Its top speed was alleged to be about 140 miles per hour, but the pilots who flew them had a saying about the PBY's speed: "It takes off at 85, it flies at 85, and it lands at 85."

Not entirely true, certainly, but pretty close. Even so, the big, ungainly seaplane had proven to be a real workhorse in the Fleet. It could stay aloft for 20 hours at a stretch, was as stable as a pool table, and could land and take off in the open sea if the swells were not too huge. To many a downed pilot floating in his rubber raft on the surface of the vast Pacific, the appearance of

"Dumbo," the colorful nickname applied to the PBY, had been the most beautiful sight in the world.

Several of the big flying boats had been hauled out of the water up onto the ramp. We strolled around them, wondering which of us would be assigned to duty in them upon graduation. Such duty was certainly arduous but very satisfying, since the PBY crews were literally the eyes and ears of the Fleet.

Learning to fly the sea-going monster, however, was a real chore.

On subsequent days, during breaks in our orientation at Corpus Christi, we watched the neophyte cadets assigned to PBYs learn the idiosyncracies of landing. If the nose was not held just so at the moment of touchdown, the big ship would either drop in with the possibility of ruptured bottom plates or it would "submarine" by burying its nose in the water with serious damage to the forward section along with thoroughly drenching the crew.

Like all learning processes, it was a slowly mastered procedure, but the cadets eventually became expert at putting the big seaplanes in the water. They also acquired the ability to taxi them around the water like outboard motorboats. Such skill was very useful in the South Pacific, where dock handling facilities were few and far between.

Our tour at Corpus Christi was to be a planned series of learning processes crammed by the Navy into as brief a time span as possible. This syllabus, as it was known, started at Cabannis Field, an outlying base from the main station at Corpus Christi.

The aircraft used to acquaint us with heavier service-type machines was the SNV trainer known as the Vultee "Vibrator." Powered by a 450-horsepower radial engine, it was a low-wing, canopy-covered type cockpit, tandem-seated, fixed landing gear airplane with the distinctive Vultee tail. The propeller was not the constant-speed, fully controllable type but rather the two-speed variety with only low and high pitch positions. The former was used for takeoff and climb, with the latter position used for cruising.

Such devices correspond roughly to the gear shift lever in an automobile. To obtain maximum horsepower from the engine for takeoff, the propeller pitch control is set in low-pitch position so the blades take a smaller bite out of the air and provide maximum rpm. As takeoff and climb are completed, the prop pitch is changed to high, which allows the propeller to take larger bites of air, causing lower engine rpm (and lower fuel consumption) and more speed for less horsepower than is possible with a fixed-pitch propeller.

At takeoff power, the combined noise of the radial engine and the low-pitch propeller shook the area for miles around. Hence the nickname "Vibrator."

After mastering the takeoff and landing characteristics of this larger machine, we were given an update of the formation flight tactics first presented back in Olathe in the venerable Stearman N2S trainers. Most of this practice was in a three-plane "V" formation with the instructor in the lead position and a cadet on either side.

One beautiful afternoon in early October with an azure sky marked only by a few puffy cumulus clouds at about 3,500 feet, we were practicing crossover maneuvers in step-up formation. In these, the two opposing wingmen (cadets) switched positions behind and on either side of the lead pilot (instructor). One cadet would slide over the top and slightly to the rear (so as not to lose visual contact) and the other underneath the leader. Such maneuvers are performed largely with the rudder by simply skidding laterally to the position desired, while holding the wings level with opposite aileron.

After several practice sessions, the procedure became fairly routine but, even so, any level of skill thus acquired was tempered with caution to avoid collision, especially in bumpy air. We were cruising along between maneuvers and I was on the right side of the instructor, slightly higher than he, just under the base of the cumulus clouds, which had become quite thick by then. My higher position suddenly thrust me into a low-hanging cloud and I could no longer see the instructor's plane.

Instinctively, I pulled up and to the right to avoid a possible collision.

Presto! I was in solid cloud, in a climbing turn and, being suddenly without the horizon, completely disoriented. The natural tendency, unfortunately, in such situations, as one watches the altimeter start to unwind and the airspeed build toward red-line, is to pull back on the stick to stop the dive.

This, of course, simply tightened the turn, developing into a "suicide spiral" if the turn was pulled tight enough. Either a high-speed stall with the resulting spin occurred or the wings parted company with the fuselage. In the latter case, the Accident Report usually read: "Debris was seen falling from the base of the clouds as the aircraft disintegrated from the high "g" forces placed upon its structure."

Once such a spiral was fully developed, exit from the aircraft was difficult because the same "g" forces compressed one into the seat of the cockpit.

Although none of us had been exposed to any instrument training yet, I had read about such disorientation in clouds and realized it was happening to me. I snapped the canopy hatch back, unfastened the radio cord from my helmet, and released the seatbelt. As I placed my hands on the side of the cockpit preparatory to leaving, the airplane burst through the base of the cloud, almost inverted and in about a 60-degree dive.

As soon as I had visual reference to the ground and the horizon again, I merely righted the airplane and leveled off.

As my heartbeat began to subside to normal and I hooked myself up to the machine again, I could see the instructor and the remaining cadet about a mile away cruising in lazy circles looking for me.

The instructor spotted me and gave the distinctive up-and-down motion with his aircraft's tail which is the standard "join-up" signal.

I eased in alongside and we proceeded back to the base. The radio remained silent. No comments about my escapade were advertised on the air.

However, after landing, the instructor inquired, "Have a little trouble in that cloud, Cadet?"

"Yes, sir," I said.

He was grateful because I could have put him on report for leading a non-instrument trained cadet into a cloud formation. As I realized it was completely unintentional, I put away my parachute and went over to Ground School without further comment.

My resolve to become an excellent instrument pilot was firmly set.

After a week's exposure to the intricacies of celestial navigation (most of which were promptly forgotten), we were all transferred to Instrument Training at a small outlying base near Beeville, Texas, about 60 miles northwest of the main station at Corpus Christi. There the mysteries of instrument flight were to be unveiled.

The tools with which we were to be taught blind flying were the Link instrument trainer and the North American SNJ aircraft. The former was just a box into which had been installed an aircraft cockpit, complete with controls, instruments, and radios. It sat on a pedestal in a room with about a dozen more just like it. It resembled a small propellerless airplane with stubby wings and tail surfaces. These latter items were strictly cosmetic additions since they had nothing whatsoever to do with the operation of the ground-bound machine.

By the use of compressed air, servo motors, and a lot of ingenuity, almost the exact simulation of flight could be produced for the student seated inside. Such student was completely isolated from any visual references outside by means of a hood, which was lowered over the whole affair while it was in use. This created the illusion (though not the bodily sensations) of actual flight.

The instructor sat at a table beside the machine and responded to the student's radio calls and his requests for information, and pointed out his errors. ("You just stalled and spun in, Cadet!")

The instructors were mostly WAVES (Women's Auxiliary Volunteer Enlisted Services) and were very patient and under-standing. All the gyrations performed by the laboring cadet in the trainer were dutifully recorded by a tracing device on the table before the instructor. This tattletale contrivance was nicknamed a "crab" because of the slow, inexorable manner in which it made its way around the paper, preserving for all to see the various "goofs" of the suffering student inside the trainer.

After mastering the actual flying of the machine through repetition of various climbs, glides, turns, etc., which required careful coordination of the simulated throttle, aileron and rudder controls, and instrument indications, one then was permitted to try cross-country flight on instruments. The "crab" would record the "airplane's" progress on a map of the area to be traversed so all errors and omissions were precisely scribed for the cadet to review once he completed his flight.

Obviously, such a device was a Godsend for learning the exacting requirements for safe passage through the elements without visual reference outside the airplane.

Psychologically, however, the Link trainer could have some strange effects.

If a learning process was not going as smoothly as it should, the claustrophobia created inside the little box could be quite maddening. Every now and then, a cadet would come out of the trainer quite suddenly without the formality of raising the hood. Others were known to pull the control wheel from its socket and proceed to beat the offending instruments from their mounts on the panel. These quirks were, fortunately, not commonplace.

The Link trainer did a marvelous job of teaching the procedures of instrument flight without the inherent danger and expense of learning them in an actual airplane.

Once we completed our syllabus in the Links, we then practiced such procedures in the back seat of the SNJ advanced trainer, the outside world completely obscured by a canvas hood. This device, when pulled into place overhead in the cockpit, left the student under it absolutely devoid of any references to his position except through the aircraft's instruments.

The SNJ was, at the time, the most sophisticated aircraft I had flown. It was used not only as an instrument trainer but for flight experience in fighter tactics and gunnery as well. For the latter it used one 30-caliber machine gun mounted on the right side just forward of the cockpit. This gun was fired through the propeller arc with the necessary synchronization gear preventing any propeller damage — most of the time. The breech locks on the guns were lubricated mostly with knuckle skin from our continual efforts to un-jam them.

A low-wing aircraft with retractable landing gear, the SNJ was powered by a Pratt & Whitney radial engine of 650 horsepower.

Although grossing some 6,500 pounds, it was highly maneuverable and could withstand the "g" forces generated in aerial gunnery practice, dive bombing, and instrument flight training.

One might wonder how high "g" forces might develop in the latter circumstance. True, in practicing instrument procedures using a full panel, which included the gyroscopic instruments (the artificial horizon and gyro compass), only the minor "g" forces encountered in a turn would result. However, if the instructor was teaching recovery from unusual positions by partial panel (also known as needle, ball, and airspeed), such high "g" forces could and often did develop quite quickly.

In this phase of training, the gyro instruments would be "caged" to avoid damage when tilted beyond their gyroscopic mechanisms' limits. If these delicate instruments were not thus immobilized, they would "tumble" and become useless, their indicating dials swirling aimlessly behind their glass faces.

Thus, the partial panel technique was used to teach the student recovery from spatial disorientation in a cloud or from severe turbulence. The procedure taught was to center the needle and ball in the turn-and-bank instrument first, then stabilize the airspeed and altitude by the control stick and throttle. This modus operandi, when executed with reasonable skill, would result in level flight once again with minimum loss of altitude.

Unfortunately, some instructors seemed to take fiendish delight in formulating new and exhilarating positions. One such diabolical individual, a Lt. (j.g.) Gerard, would perform a really bizarre aerobatic maneuver. He would haul the airplane up and over in a normal loop but upon reaching the top of the loop in an inverted position, rather than completing the loop or rolling upright in an Immelmann turn, he thrust the stick suddenly forward while he pushed one of the rudders to its limit. As the airplane literally tumbled down through the air, he would direct the unfortunate student: "Okay, Cadet, recover."

However, by merely following the prescribed method — i.e., centering the needle and ball with lateral stick and appropriate rudder control, then stabilizing the airspeed and altimeter with fore and aft movement of the control stick — recovery could usually be effected in about 2,500 feet. Hopefully, the instructor would not enter such a maneuver below 5,000 feet, just in case the student wound it up in an inverted spin, with the resulting recovery difficulty expending all the altitude.

Such unorthodox treatment for both airplane and student may seen unduly harsh. But each of us learned recovery techniques quickly under those imposed stresses.

The final phase of our syllabus in the Corpus Christi Naval Air Training Complex was at the auxiliary field at Kingsville, Texas, located on the Gulf edge of the sprawling King Ranch. We were told by some of the local gentry that we could fly to the extent of the range of most of the training planes and still be on the King Ranch. Although this was not entirely true, the ranch was indeed "quite a spread," even by Texas standards.

In addition to the SNJ advanced trainers at Kingsville, there was also the N3N Navy primary trainer, which had been in general use before the N2S Stearman we used at Olathe. The N3N was the Navy's own design, manufactured at the Naval Aircraft Factory in Philadelphia as a standard primary trainer. The entire airplane was stoutly made to take the expected normal abuse of neophyte student pilots. This was particularly true of the stalwart landing gear, which could withstand the bone-rattling "whump" when a student dropped it in from about ten feet.

The N3N was the only airplane in which I ever experienced an outside loop, although I didn't perform it; I was simply along for the ride.

My instructor in advanced fighter tactics at Kingsville was Lt. (j.g.) Nielsen, whose fellow instructors had nicknamed him

"Cowboy." The moniker, I was to discover, was entirely appropriate.

A tall, gangly, good-natured Texan from San Angelo, he flew an airplane with the same efficiency — and ferocity — that he rode horses back on the family ranch. He was, most certainly, an excellent aerobatic pilot and had that unique ability to impart his personal style and technique to his students. He usually instructed in the SNJ advanced trainer. But on this particular morning, Lt. Nielsen asked, "You supposed to fly this morning?"

"No, sir," I replied.

"Want to go along with me and punch a few holes in the sky with the N3N?"

"Yes, sir!" My response was enthusiastic since Nielsen's prowess with the big yellow biplane was well known.

We settled into the tandem seats with our parachutes as cushions, and he fired up the big radial engine.

Pulling onto the runway, he lifted off at about 75 miles an hour and we headed west over open country, climbing easily to about 8,000 feet.

We then took turns in doing loops, rolls, and Immelmann turns with him initiating some additional aerobatics completely new to me. The man was superb; he and the machine were perfectly matched.

Taking the stick, he rolled the airplane inverted and stuck the nose straight down. Normally, when this is done, the pilot pulls the throttle back and allows gravity alone to accelerate the airplane.

Not Nielsen. He left it wide open!

The wind began screaming through the wires and struts bracing the wings. Their presence was most welcome.

Not until the big trainer reached its 190-mph terminal velocity did Nielsen slowly ease the stick back, bringing it out of its headlong dash to earth. Then he rolled inverted and pushed the stick forward. Once again, we streaked upward, the tremendous negative "g" forces pushing our blood supply into our heads. My eyeballs felt as if they were preparing to leave their sockets, like those of a deep-sea rock codfish when it is suddenly brought to the surface. We completed the loop in an upright position just above stalling speed.

Nielsen looked back at me and grinned like some schoolkid who had just shot a spitball in class and didn't get caught. Picking up the Gosport speaking tube and looking at me in his rearview mirror, he asked, "Ever do one of those before?"

I shook my head.

"This is one of the few airplanes that can take an outside loop," he said. "I just thought you'd like to see what it's like."

Satisfied, he rolled the airplane on its back once again and aimed it toward Kingsville. Rotating upright again, he entered the traffic pattern and rolled the wheels smoothly on the pavement. A real pilot's pilot!

Parking the N3N on the back part of the ramp, we climbed out and walked over to the squadron office.

"Well, back to work, Cadet," Nielsen said. "Thanks for being company!"

At Kingsville we were taught how to fight with an airplane. Day after day we practiced aerial gunnery, dive bombing, night and day formation tactics, all in the ubiquitous SNJ trainer. We even renewed our acquaintance with the infamous "Mark III plotting board," with which we first wrestled at Olathe in primary training.

This extraordinarily inaccurate device was little more than a transparent piece of plexiglass about a foot square on which parallel and vertical lines were printed. A tiny, hand-operated circular computer was mounted in one corner. With this Rube Goldberg contraption we were supposed to be able to find our way to a target off a carrier, do our job on the enemy, and then find our way back to the carrier before acquiring an acute case of fuel starvation.

If the carrier moved (which it always did), if the wind changed (which it always did), if we sustained engine damage (which would slow down the airplane), we were supposed to apply the proper corrections on our trusty plotting board and, with Lady Luck with us all the way, return to base.

In practice, trying to work the navigation problem with the plotting board on your lap, fly formation in the airplane, guess the wind drift, and hold a compass heading made most navigational training flights exercises in futility and frustration. Fortunately, we all knew the identifying landmarks around Kingsville by the time we reached this point in the syllabus, so we passed the course. I can't help believing that Navy brass placed this phase of the training last for that very reason. Otherwise, no one would have graduated.

Eventually, we did pass all the courses, received our Navy wings of gold at an appropriate ceremony, and became Naval Aviators with the rank of second lieutenant in the Marine Corps or ensign in the Navy.

We were not actually given a choice in this selection, although we were asked to state our preference on a pre-graduation information questionnaire. I had previously placed in my file my desire to be a Marine with operational duties as fighter pilot, the ulterior motive for which was the fact that I knew Marines flew the Corsair. The reiteration of this request apparently was the necessary catalyst that moved the yeoman in charge of the process to type my orders accordingly.

There was even a rumor that only the "upper ten percent" of the class was commissioned in the Marines. This hypothesis was quickly dismissed by our squadron mates, who were anointed as ensigns, with such comments as: "You guys know well enough that they dump all our names in a hat and pull out enough to make the monthly quota for the 'Gyrenes'!" Their conclusion was entirely plausible but we, of course, preferred the former theory. Thus, my operational designation: fighter pilot, with orders to United States Naval Auxiliary Air Station, Green Cove Springs, Florida, for fighter training in the new Navy F4U Corsairs.

We arrived on the train from Corpus Christi (this time it had really been Pullman sleeper accommodations) at three in the afternoon. For the final half-hour of the ride to Florida, we had all been at the train windows ogling the F4U Corsairs, F6F Hellcats, and F4F Wildcats entering traffic to land at Jacksonville Naval Air Station. My Marine contingent boarded a bus immediately and soon we were entering the gate of USNAAS Green Cove Springs.

As soon as our barracks assignments were made, we stowed our gear and immediately departed for the flight line to check out the "bent-wing monsters" in which we were to receive combat training. Rounding the corner of the operations hangar, we fixed our gaze on four F4Us parked on the ramp: huge, dirty, scarred, and beautiful. We took turns scaling the right side (we had always entered cockpits on the left side before) by means of steps and handholds in the sides of the fuselage with little spring-loaded covers that retracted inward when we pushed them.

Settling into the cockpit for the first time, I grasped the control column and fondled the throttle quadrant with its accompanying mixture and propeller controls that gave dominance over the 2,000 horses in the big round engine in front of me.

Then I looked up and observed the thirteen feet of fuselage between me and the propeller. No wonder this airplane had acquired, among others, the nickname "Hose-Nose." Taxiing would be a major maneuver.

After the Navy's seemingly interminable orientations, cockpit checkouts, inflight movies, and endless "do's" and "don't's," we were assigned to "flights" of seven pilots each, plus a combat veteran instructor. Our mentor was Mr. Flournoy, the Navy lieutenant (j.g.) who had shepherded me back to Palatka after my unfortunate experience with the tow cable. Just returned from duty in the South Pacific, he was a superb flyer and an outstanding teacher. He was conscientious to a fault in his unflagging tenacity while instilling in all of us the finer points of our deadly future occupation. His sole ambition seemed to be that of teaching us to do our job and survive.

My name eventually appeared opposite F4U-1 No. 07532 on the flight board for 13 March 1944. The kindly crew chief made sure that I was thoroughly "hooked up" to all the systems in the cockpit and stood by on the wing while I fired the starter cartridge. Such starting mechanisms, used on most service aircraft engines of the time, used a small cylinder and piston arrangement coupled to the engine's crankshaft, with the power supplied by the gases from an exploding cartridge, like an oversized shotgun shell, to spin the propeller.

The shell was placed into a breech on the right side of the fuselage at the rear of the engine compartment. The device was closed, locked in place, and the access door in the fuselage shut and latched. After priming the engine, I signalled that all was ready and pushed the starter switch. Pa-shoosh! The giant Pratt & Whitney R-2800 roared to life. I quickly pulled the throttle back to idle so the resulting hurricane winds wouldn't blow the crew chief off the wing. He obviously was accustomed to such blasts at the hands of new pilots and maintained a firm grip on the recessed handholds. As soon as I throttled back, he climbed down, moved off to the side, saluted smartly, and backed away.

Releasing the brakes, I nursed the throttle forward, moved away from the line of Corsairs, and asked the tower for clearance to the runway. In order to effect some semblance of forward vision past the Corsair's long nose, continuous S-turns were necessary. I soon discovered the disk brakes overheated, making them virtually worthless after a few minutes' use in taxiing, a characteristic Mr. Flournoy had mentioned to us. Consequently, any attempt to run the engine up to check the magnetos had the Corsair creeping forward even while I literally stood on the brakes. Eventually, I completed the takeoff checklist and advised the tower I was ready to "scramble" (the code word for "take off").

Receiving clearance, I pushed the throttle steadily to the stop and eased my feet down from the brakes to the rudder pedals. Acceleration was immediate and unbelievable as my right foot pressed on more and more rudder to counteract the torque of the unleashed fury in front of me. The ground dropped away at between 65 and 70 knots, and I reached down to the left to raise the landing gear handle. As the wheels came up into the wells under the wing, I reached up and pulled the canopy to its closed position. I then glanced at the airspeed and rate of climb indicators. The airplane was doing 150 knots and going up at 2,000 feet a minute! I started pulling things back; throttle to 36 inches of manifold pressure and propeller to 2,600 rpm. Things began to calm down.

Departing the traffic pattern I climbed to 10,000 feet and just flew the machine for a while. The transition from the 650 horsepower in the SNJ to the 2,000 horsepower in the Corsair could best be described as exhilarating. I was not prepared for the absolute smoothness of the R-2800's eighteen cylinders as opposed to the comparative rumble of the nine in the SNJ powerplant.

After some turning maneuvers and mild aerobatics, such as wing-overs and chandelles, I backed off the throttle, put the landing gear and flaps down, and practiced a half dozen "landings" at 10,000 feet. While easing the stick all the way back and holding the airplane straight with the rudders, the usual buffeting warned of the impending stall before it dropped off on the left wing. Satisfied that I could get it down in one piece, I retracted the gear and flaps and headed for "Green Base" (the radio code name for our base at Green Cove Springs).

Using the prescribed wartime code for fighters, I called the tower, "Green Base, this is Cisco 2-1, orbiting outboard. Request pancake one chick."

The response was equally terse: "Cisco 2-1, this is Green Base. Cleared to orbit inboard and pancake."

Sliding the hatch back, I entered downwind, put the gear handle in the "down" position once more, and dropped 20 degrees of flaps. Easing around to final approach at 75 knots, I added full flaps, flared to three-point attitude, and touched down just past the runway numbers. With 4,000 feet of asphalt, I just let it roll, pampering the temperamental disk brakes until the last 1,000 feet, where I gingerly applied my toes to the upper part of the rudder pedals. The disks worked once again since they had cooled during the flight, and I soon slowed to taxi speed. Remembering to open the cowl flaps, I taxied back to the ramp in a state of complete euphoria. It was hard to remind myself of the landing problems that had plagued this aircraft before it was finally accepted by the Navy.

The Corsair, as was the case with all Navy carrier fighters, was normally landed in the three-point, fully stalled attitude to allow the tail hook to catch the arresting wire on the carrier deck. Its touchdown speed was quite low, only 67 knots, an amazing engineering accomplishment when one realized its top speed was 335 knots at 25,000 feet. This low landing speed was achieved by means of huge, hydraulically operated wing flaps (irreverently referred to by pilots as "barn doors") that had the effect of airbrakes with full aileron control ability maintained at such low speeds.

A tiny pencil-thin spoiler had been placed just outboard of the wing root oil cooler openings. This permitted sufficient power to be applied to maintain forward speed as the aircraft was landed. Before these spoilers were added, the earlier models of the Corsair had earned a rather unsavory reputation as killers due to their tendency to roll inverted if too much power was applied on landing, as happened when a pilot was directed to "go around." The tremendous torque of the big engine and propeller combination would cause a violent, uncontrollable roll to the left with usually fatal results. The spoilers, causing both wing roots to stall before the outboard portions, very neatly eliminated this objectionable characteristic.

Before these spoilers were installed, Navy top brass had decided that the fatality rate of their new fighter was unacceptable. So, since tooling and production facilities were complete, contracts signed, and the planes were desperately needed in the Fleet for the Pacific Campaign, the Corsair was assigned to the Marine Corps. Marine operations were usually land-based, so it was felt that two-wheel landings could be used rather than the three-point landings required for carriers.

In this type of landing, a higher speed could be maintained until touchdown since the aircraft was flown right down to the runway until the main gear made contact, at which time the flaps were retracted and the plane quit flying. The pilot then lowered the tail and applied the brakes, resulting in a smooth airliner-type landing. Of course, this landing procedure required considerably more landing distance than was available on a carrier. Even so, the Marines thus acquired an excellent new piece of equipment for their island-hopping campaign in the Pacific and I, as a Marine pilot, was here to learn how to use this new "weapon" most effectively.

For two months we practiced all the deadly techniques then in vogue for fighter pilots. Although we were taught dive bombing, strafing runs, bomber escort using the "Thach weave" whereby the fighter sections (two planes) would cross back and forth over our bomber formations while they droned along toward their targets, and night formation tactics, most of our time was spent in aerial gunnery tactics — day after day of gunnery runs on the tow target off the coast of Florida. Each of us became highly skilled not only in flying the Corsair but also in the use of its six 50-caliber machine guns that spewed forth 3,600 rounds a minute. This awesome firepower, boresighted to converge at a thousand feet, was already proving to be devastatingly destructive in the Pacific.

Finally, Mr. Flournoy taught us how to land on a carrier. Even though the procedure was not part of the Marine syllabus, he explained, "You may come back to your island base someday to find that enemy bombers have made the runway unusable. So, if there's a carrier nearby, I want you to know how to land on it."

He would park his Corsair on the left side of the approach end of the runway and, as we came around to land, he would "talk us down" on his radio, much the same as the landing signal officer would do with colored paddles on the deck of a carrier. We would come around in a circling approach just above stalling speed, listening to his instructions and, when he said "Cut!" we closed the throttle and banged the airplane down on a spot marked to simulate the first wire on a carrier. If we were too high or too fast, he would "wave us off" with a curt "Go around!" It was hard, sweaty work, but from him I learned a valuable survival technique from a truly dedicated instructor.

Then, on 7 May 1944, Mr. Flournoy announced our next destination: "Report to the Commanding Officer, United States Marine Corps Air Station, Cherry Point, North Carolina, for duty assignment."

Retrofit

The sprawling Marine Air Station, located in a reclaimed swamp on the east coast of North Carolina, was ideal for training for duty in the South Pacific islands, for it had the prerequisite combination of mosquitos, humidity, and mildew.

After a brief stint in an operational squadron at an outlying base from the main station at Cherry Point, we were prepared both psychologically and technologically for work as fighter pilots. We were ready for duty in the South Pacific.

A few days before Christmas, 1944, my roommate, Melvin, burst through the door.

"The orders are in!" he yelled.

"Where are we going?"

"I heard they've picked about fifty guys to go to New York and Columbus, Ohio, to the Ferry Command. I guess they want Marines to deliver new Corsairs to the West Coast."

I asked, "Which did we get, New York or Columbus, and when do we leave?"

"Well," he replied, "I'm not going. My orders are for overseas duty."

Melvin and I had been in the same training unit since pre-flight days the previous summer. He was a good friend and an excellent pilot. We had hoped, when the time came, to do combat patrol together. We shared the same philosophy. Neither of us was of a particularly belligerent nature, but since our country was in a battle for survival, both physically and ideologically, we were willing to fight for that survival with whatever skills we possessed.

"As to when we leave, it's the first of the year, I believe," he said. "At least, that's what the word is over at the office."

"Do we get leave for Christmas?"

"I guess so," he answered, so I suggested that we walk over to the Adjutant's Office to check on the exact nature of the orders. Melvin's were to report to a West Coast point of embarkation for overseas duty.

Mine were short and to the point: I was to report to the Commanding Officer, U.S. Naval Ferry Squadron, Columbus, Ohio, December 29, 1944, for duty "involving flying." With a shock, I realized I was one of the pilots going to the Ferry Command. I was crushed.

Such orders seemed so illogical. Here we were, all 400 of us fully trained as Marine fighter pilots (though still categorized as simply "Naval Aviator"), marking time in the Marines' catch-all squadron, MWSS-9 (Marine Wing Service Squadron 9) at Cherry Point. Certainly, military decisions allow one little control over his own destiny. This basic characteristic of a fighting organization is even more pronounced in wartime. My disappointment at not being sent overseas to do the job for which I had been trained for the last six months was apparently obvious to Melvin.

He immediately attempted to counter my frustration.

"Hey, Bones," he said, using his nickname for my six-foot, one-inch, 160-pound frame, "It's the cream of all the duty. You just ride around the country in brand-new airplanes and get paid extra for it."

This reference to extra pay had to do with the per diem travel expense money that ferry pilots were alleged to receive while on the road.

Since I had acquired an automobile while at Cherry Point, I drove to Columbus after spending my Christmas leave with my family in East Tennessee. After a near-disaster with a bus on an icy bridge in Ohio (we missed each other by inches), I arrived at the Naval Air Station at Port Columbus, the Municipal Airport of Ohio's capital city, on 29 December 1944.

Checking into the squadron was accomplished with a "checklist" which, when first observed, seemed endless: housing, eating facilities, flight equipment, pay procedure (we were all most interested in this item as we had just finished Christmas leave and were flat broke), and the inevitable orientation meetings.

Our initial welcome was conducted by a Commander Richardson, who was cordial enough and did his best to familiarize us with the intricacies of delivering the Navy's airplanes promptly and safely to their designated destinations around the country. We soon discovered, however, that a previous Marine detachment at this squadron had permanently warped the reputation of the operation; some of our predecessors had shown a propensity for performing slow rolls a few feet above the runway, practicing assorted acrobatics over the heart of the city, and regularly engaging in simulated strafing runs on some of the local countryside's dairy cattle, vehicular traffic, and railroad trains.

These activities, conducted in a civilian environment, had caused serious doubts in the Navy's command level as to the advisability of using fighter jockeys for the staid, conservative job of delivering airplanes. Nevertheless, Washington had decreed that, since we were almost uniquely qualified to ferry Corsairs to the West Coast staging areas because of our personal experience with the big new fighter's flight characteristics, we were given the assignment. Commander Richardson and his staff felt they must indoctrinate us with the niceties of proper ferry pilot decorum. He did this with considerable diplomatic aplomb, and concluded his remarks by assuring us that we were "vitally necessary to the war effort" and he was sure we would "build a record of deliveries of which we could be proud."

Emerging from our orientation lecture, we discovered a howling blizzard had descended upon Columbus. The snow covering the wings and fuselages of the Corsairs standing in line awaiting delivery gave the warbirds an unhealthy appearance, ghostly and useless. Even so, I was awed by the enormity of this ferry operation. The fighters were manufactured at the factory in Akron and were flown to Columbus by "inflight pilots." The Navy formally accepted delivery and installed the fighting gear − i.e., guns, radios, and any special equipment − after which the fully equipped airplanes were test-flown again by the Navy's acceptance pilots for about three or four hours. If all was well, the birds went to the ferry unit's flight line for delivery to the Fleet.

The blizzard lasted three days, during which time we were treated to various training films and further indoctrination lessons as to the proper methods for safely moving airplanes via airways under the supervision of civilian air traffic control from Point A to Point B. Like all pilots, we were chafing to get on with the flying even though we realized this knowledge was necessary if we were to be at all compatible with the civilian system.

My baptism into the actual workings of aircraft delivery started early on the morning after the blizzard had dissipated. There was a tap on my shoulder and a pleasant but authoritative voice asked my name.

I turned to observe a tall Navy full lieutenant who, though outranking my gold bars by two full grades, smiled and said, "I'm Bill Ronson. It looks like we'll be taking an R4D from Oklahoma City to San Diego. Your orders are over in Operations." R4D was the Navy's designation for the famous airline twin-engine work-horse transport, the Douglas DC-3. Its basic design originated in 1932 with its predecessor, the DC-2. With various refinements and engine configurations, it evolved into the staple civilian airliner, carrying from 20 to 25 passengers in marketable comfort around the country at almost three miles a minute.

Civilian and Navy regulations required a pilot and copilot for such aircraft. The latter job was to be mine for the next two days. The entire output of the Douglas plant at Oklahoma City was now being acquired by the Armed Forces for the massive logistic requirements of war. We were to deliver a new R4D-6 to the Fleet operation on the West Coast.

"How do we get to Oklahoma City?" I asked.

"Probably Mr. McDonald will run us down there in the squadron's R4D," he said.

After picking up our orders, Ronson and I walked across the aircraft ramp to the squadron's own transport, a well-used R4D whose former airline insignia was recognizable in a couple of places where the Navy paint job was peeling. We climbed aboard, each with our parachute pack and green zipper bag that held, we hoped, enough underwear, shirts, and socks to last the trip. After stowing this luggage, we took our seats, which were set up much the same as those in civilian passenger airlines.

Ronson introduced me to some of his colleagues from the squadron who were going to ride with us. They were continuing on beyond Oklahoma City to Corpus Christi, where they would bring back some aging Twin-Beech executive transports to Wichita for overhaul. Even though various ranks were present, we felt the easy camaraderie that is universal among aviators. Still, this was to be a learning experience for me, and I tried to pick up bits of useful information about my new job from these men, who were obviously masters of their profession.

I also received my first lesson in cold weather operations. Winter in Columbus, Ohio, is miserably cold. Buildings in the city are, of course, constructed to withstand the most severe winters. Unfortunately, aircraft lubricants are not. Engine oil takes on the consistency of molasses and is quite useless for performing its normal function of eliminating friction between moving metal parts. What is worse, oil collects in the bottom cylinders of the big radial engines, such as those on the DC-3 and Corsair, if they are not turned over. If an attempt is made to start the engine before pulling the propeller through several times to redistribute the oil, the resulting hydraulic pressure in those bottom cylinders can be devastating to cylinder heads, connecting rods, and pistons.

The trip to Oklahoma City took about five hours. However, since we acquired an hour by our westerly movement into another time zone, it was noon when we pilots all gave a thumbs-up gesture to Mr. McDonald as he eased the wheels onto the concrete runway at Tinker Field.

Ronson and I departed the comfort of the R4D's cabin and walked over to the Navy's office to arrange ground transportation to the Douglas facility on the field. After refueling ourselves at the lunch counter, we walked out to the delivery hangar, where stood the Navy transport we were to deliver to San Diego. It was painted the stark olive drab in vogue at the time, but was still obviously brand-new.

As Ronson meticulously checked out the airplane, he made certain that I realized the importance of making such preflight checks of all new aircraft. Although the reputation of the assembly line that produced this one was excellent, glitches could occur and it was up to us to find them while still on the ground. The final factory inspectors appeared to have done their job well and the big transport seemed to be ready for service.

"Did you ever copilot one of these before?" Ronson asked.

"The ride down here was the first time I was ever in one," I answered somewhat lamely.

"Well, well," Ronson said, with a smile. "This should be interesting." Still, he didn't seem too perturbed at my complete lack of training for the job at hand. I soon discovered why. Although the regulations required a copilot on this aircraft, he was completely capable of flying it himself, so my job was largely that of an interested observer − or, as aviators say, "a sandbag." Even so, Ronson explained the idiosyncracies of this particular airplane. It was totally different from my usual steed, the Corsair.

There was, of course, literally no comparison.

Both machines were capable of flight. There the similarity ended. The transport was designed to haul people and/or cargo in an efficient and safe manner, while the Corsair's *raison d'etre* was aerial combat. The single engine of the Corsair equaled the power of both those on the wings of the R4D, and its top speed was twice that of the slower transport. Still, whatever it lacked in speed and maneuverability, the R4D more than matched in creature comforts and ease of handling.

After carefully checking the magnetos and propeller controls at the end of the runway, Ronson asked for takeoff clearance from the tower. Then he eased forward the two big throttles on the center quadrant between us and the transport slowly gathered speed. I watched the airspeed indicator needle go by 75 mph as Ronson ever so gently tugged the yoke and lifted us into Oklahoma's crisp winter air.

"Want to get the gear? It's that lever on the floor. Just pull it," Ronson said routinely, getting me into the act.

With the wheels tucked neatly into the engine nacelles, we climbed southwest toward El Paso at 130 mph. Reaching 8,500 feet, Ronson pulled the throttles and propellers back to cruise power and trimmed the ship for level flight. The airspeed settled down at about 160 mph, which meant our true airspeed was just under 180, after correcting the normal altitude error of about 2 mph per thousand feet above sea level. Ronson observed me checking the speed and smiled again.

"Not such a slow-poke after all, huh, Mr. Copilot?" he asked. "About the same as your bent-wing monster at slow cruise power."

I leaned back into the comfortable seat. "Wonder what kind of slow roll it'll do?"

"I don't know about slow rolls," Ronson said, laughing. "But some guy in Alaska looped one once and it held together okay." I would have reason to remember this remark later in the day.

We flew over some small mountains, really no more than a series of little humps, jutting up from the West Texas plains. As we approached them, Ronson reached over and snapped on a switch under an instrument that looked like a regular altimeter.

"This is a good place to see how this gadget works," he explained. "The guy at the factory said it's one of the new radio altimeters. It's supposed to tell you the actual distance from the ground using a radio signal projected at the ground. By measuring the time required for the signal to make the round trip back to the airplane, the distance (altitude) could be computed with extreme accuracy."

I watched the needle of the instrument fluctuate as we flew over the group of humps in the terrain beneath us. Instantaneously we were given the exact distance separating us from those land formations below.

"Handy gadget," I offered. "Especially when you're making a descent or an approach in weather and on the gauges."

"Amen," he agreed.

Cruising at 10,500 feet in relatively smooth air for a West Texas afternoon, we soon went by Red Bluff Reservoir, where Ronson made a minor adjustment to the elevator trim tab and snapped on the automatic pilot. The airplane quivered a bit as the servo units of the "third pilot" took over the job of flying.

He stretched and said, "I'm going back in the main cabin a while to check out some equipment, so watch for traffic and don't hit any Texas longhorns," he said.

He was unbuckling his seatbelt when the aircraft made a violent roll.

Luckily, the seatbelt remained fastened or he might have broken his neck. I grabbed the control wheel. A trained aerobatic pilot, I allowed the big ship to roll on through 360 degrees and, when we came upright, I stopped the roll by overriding the autopilot.

As soon as he could reassemble his composure, Ronson helped me with the wheel and calmly snapped off the automatic pilot. The whole episode had consumed maybe ten seconds.

"Well, we know now what kind of slow roll it'll do," he deadpanned. "Any problems?"

"No, but I'd at least like to read this airplane's Aerobatic Manual before I do another one," I replied.

"I'm just glad you were there. It's been a while since I've rolled an airplane."

"What do you suppose caused it?" I wanted to know just how far one could trust these new-fangled autopilots, as I had heard of such shenanigans before.

"Oh, I suppose one of the servo motor switches is on the blink," Ronson said. "We can report it at San Diego so they can check it out. I don't believe I'll report the resulting maneuver, though." He smiled and looked straight ahead. I was still holding the wheel and the color had returned to my knuckles. Once again, he announced a visit to the cabin, unbuckled his seatbelt, and disappeared through the cockpit door, this time leaving the flying to me.

"Go just to the south of Guadalupe Peak there, and hold about 260 degrees for El Paso. I'll be back in a few minutes."

The twin engines were almost perfectly synchronized at about 1,750 rpm and the muffled drone provided a very effective lullaby. The sun's rays were now almost directly in my eyes but, by sitting completely erect in the seat and pulling the sun visor down, I could still avoid most of their late afternoon glare.

These dazzling horizontal shafts of light piercing through a hazy sky could be one of the most aggravating and fatiguing factors in westerly cross-country flight. One's eyes instinctively squint and try to reject the assault on the optic nerves as the ability to observe the territory ahead steadily deteriorated. Averting my gaze to the side or to some object in the cockpit helped only momentarily. Some pilots, myself included, eventually succumbed to the temptation to place an open sectional map up against the windshield and thus shut out the afflicting brilliance. Certainly this was not condoned by safety regulations, but then the authors of those regulations didn't do much flying into the West Texas sun.

I had the Salt Flat radio directional beam's steady signal in the earphones and, as a sudden silence indicated the station was directly beneath, I reached over and eased the throttles back to start the descent into El Paso. The altimeter slowly started to unwind at about 500 feet per minute. Since the altitude of the runway required a landing pattern of 5,000 feet, we should be properly aligned in about ten minutes or so.

The cockpit door opened and Ronson slid his lean six-foot two-inch frame back into the left seat, and fastened his seatbelt. He did not immediately take over the controls.

"Ever been to El Paso?" he asked.

"Once, when we were on a family vacation returning from California on the train," I said, remembering that trip. "We had a four-hour layover and went across the border to Juarez. It was my first venture out of the United States."

"Yeah, it's some place," Ronson said, knowingly.

"My most vivid memory of El Paso, though, is not about Juarez," I said. "It's the lunch we had at a little cafe down the street from the El Paso railroad station. On the edge of the plate was a large serving of horseradish sauce and it looked exactly like coleslaw to me. Since I really like coleslaw, I lifted a whole forkful into my mouth. Hoo! Hah! Huge swallows of iced tea finally eased the effect, but I won't soon forget that stuff."

Ronson laughed, then asked, "Ever try Mexican chili peppers?"

"No, I don't think so."

"Oh, you would remember it if you had," Ronson said, grinning broadly. "They make horseradish seem like ice cream by comparison."

The conversation continued on food as we descended into El Paso. Ronson went through the landing checklist with me and planted the big airplane squarely on the runway numbers. The man was good. I wondered which airline would be blessed with his services when the war was over.

Ronson personally supervised the line crew as the plane was secured for the night, and we strode over to the Operations Office to check in.

Several Navy pilots recognized Ronson and the usual friendly chatter ensued.

"What're you and the 'gyrene' learning to fly this trip, Ronson?" one of them asked. "You've gotta watch these fighter jockeys, y'know. They'll try to loop the Queen Mary."

Ronson and I exchanged wry smiles but kept straight faces as he signed the register sheet for our local hotel accommodations. Our abode for the night turned out to be an ancient hotel recently remodeled to serve as a way station for pilots. The house restaurant was not fancy, but it was clean and the food was good. The beds were comfortable and there was a bath down the hall on each floor.

Several of our colleagues elected to go across the border into Mexico after dinner for fun and games. Ronson and I declined the invitation to join them. He had some letters to write, and I wanted to take a stroll around the area to assure myself that my leg muscles were still capable of mobility after 1,200 miles and seven hours of sitting in one position. Also, I wanted some time to reflect on this first day of my new job. I decided that I liked it.

As Melvin had observed back at Cherry Point, it was, indeed, the cream of the duty.

Mornings at El Paso are sights to savor. The city is named appropriately enough. A break in the mountain range just west of the city provides convenient passage for the Rio Grande River to change from the north-to-south direction that it has followed down from Albuquerque to an easterly heading. From the pass ("El Paso") through the mountains, it continues its meandering to the Gulf of Mexico and establishes the southern border of Texas. The morning sun glinting on the eastern face of the mountains and the surface of the river is the reincarnation of all the prettiest scenery in hundreds of Western movies lodged in my memory.

After breakfast and the bus ride to the airport, we filed a flight plan for San Diego and went out to preflight the R4D. It checked out okay, and my second lesson in ferrying airplanes began.

"Gear up," Ronson called, as we resumed our westward journey at 9 a.m.

We were both a bit sleepy, as some of our more wayward colleagues had returned to the hotel from their explorations of the international delights of Juarez quite late and our respite from the previous day's travel had suffered several interruptions.

Such late night excursions were not the practice of seasoned ferry pilots. Almost invariably such activities caused them to be late arriving at the airport for the day's flight. Also, the efficiency of the pilots was somewhat impaired by the previous night's overindulgence. Such impairment was considered by the local FCLO (Ferry Control Liaison Officer) to be a gross infraction of regulations. The Army Air Corps captain at El Paso had developed an almost paranoid antipathy for pilots who showed up late and considerably the worse for the evening's revelry.

Their Service career, if the FCLO chose, could be altered drastically for such derelictions to duty. His wrath was customarily ameliorated by impassioned pleas from senior officers on behalf of their more brash compatriots to the effect that:

"It won't happen again, Captain. He didn't realize what he was drinking or how late it was. Besides, think of the investment the Government has in him by now."

Or, "He missed the last bus because he had to wait for the laundry to open so he could get some shirts he left here last time."

This last was often a true story. I was soon to discover that one of the chronic banes of a ferry pilot's existence was the laundry and dry-cleaning problem. Shirts, underwear, socks, and even entire uniforms would be awaiting our return on the next trip in cities and towns all over the country. We soon learned to share items of apparel, maps, and even sums of money ("Until I get paid, back at the base") It was remarkable how few of these debts remained unpaid.

Our interdependence on one another fostered complete integrity in such matters. At times, though, such interchanges of clothing could be ludicrous.

The duty officers at most of the Officers' Mess Halls on the various military air bases could be rather picky when it came to allowing us to enter without regulation attire. Therefore, it was not unusual for lieutenants in the Army Air Corps or Marines suddenly to acquire the rank — and the blouse (Navy terminology for "coat") — of a Navy lieutenant (j.g.) so he could eat. We often suspected the aforementioned duty officers knew exactly what was going on, but since we were making a bona fide effort to comply with the rules they would go along with such chicanery.

When time did not permit such relays for meals, certain food items could be spirited out in navigation bags for one's hungry colleagues by the fortunate one in proper uniform. Such procedures are not found in military regulation manuals but effectively kept the machinery humming.

The R4D performed the task on that morning for which it was designed. We had acquired a passenger for this leg of the trip — a member of the Women's Army Corps (WAC) going home to Los Angeles on leave. Such hitchhiking was permitted in the ferry service as long as the passenger was a member of the Armed Forces and was on approved travel orders. The only additional requisite was a parachute, which could usually be obtained at the Operations desk and was checked in at the rider's destination. No instructions for its use were ever offered, so the efficacy of this requirement was, to say the least, questionable.

As soon as we were trimmed out for cruise at 10,500 feet, Ronson turned to me and said, "Better check on our customer."

I unbuckled my seatbelt and went back into the cabin where our passenger was already fast asleep, the parachute pack performing a useful function for a change, as a pillow. The cabin was designed for cargo, so only a few bucket seats were installed along the walls, making her sleeping facilities somewhat less than comfortable. It was probably her first leave since joining the Service, I reasoned, and she was enjoying dreams of going home.

She was a petite blonde whose regulation Army skirt and blouse didn't do too much to enhance the curves of femininity obviously present beneath them. I couldn't help pondering the ludicrous thought of just how she would react if she were suddenly told to strap on the parachute in the event of some emergency. The leg straps would preclude any pretense of modesty, so she would probably elect to go down with the ship. However, the air was perfectly smooth and the aircraft seemed suspended, so her sleep was quite sound.

I returned to the cockpit and reported that all was well with our passenger.

Our course took us just south of Deming, New Mexico, and paralleled the busy railroad tracks from El Paso westward. The railroad towns of Separ, Wilna, and Lordsburg passed beneath our wings. Several freight trains could be seen inching their way across the terrain, some over a mile in length, probably doing about 80 mph.

I couldn't help comparing our speed and freedom of movement with that of the iron horses below. Our tonnage capacity, though, was minuscule today compared to theirs. Literally thousands of tons of cargo were moving steadily on schedule across the country by the marvelous American railroad system. In addition, all cross-country pilots at one time or another develop an affinity for railroads. With their straight rails and gently curving roadbeds, they make very effective visual links from one town to another and eventually lead to, or close by, an airport. In times of low visibility, railroads can be lifesavers to the lost pilot looking for a landing strip. Unfortunately, railroads frequently make use of tunnels to negotiate their way through mountainous terrain. Care must be used, therefore, when using these so-called iron compasses so that no attempt be made to follow the rails through. Such attempts are guaranteed to make the headlines in the local newspapers.

Our estimated time enroute (ETE) from El Paso to San Diego was just under four hours. The season's weather provided excellent visibility, and Ronson continuously pointed out various landmarks along the way which that would be of navigational assistance to me in subsequent flights. He knew I would frequently be flying a single-seat Corsair and, therefore, would be doing my own navigation.

"See those two little knobs there on top of that mountain?" he asked, pointing to the left of our course where I could make out two sharply defined, rounded peaks.

"If you fly just to the right of those, you'll hit Willcox, Arizona, on the nose," he said. "The same course goes just north of Lemmon and Mica Mountains this side of Tucson."

He then proceeded to make me aware of a hidden gas stop at Coolidge, Arizona. We didn't need it that day, but he said I would probably be stopping there for fuel in Corsairs and quite conscientiously pointed out the best way to pick it out of its concealment in the desert terrain.

The Gila River Valley slid beneath us, and we went by several training fields as we approached Yuma.

"Keep your eyes open through here," Ronson cautioned. "These bases are swarming with student pilots and instructors who aren't necessarily watching for other traffic."

As he said this, a formation flight of four Vultee "Vibrator" single-engine trainers went by us from right to left, seemingly completely oblivious to our presence.

"See what I mean?" he observed.

I reminded myself that although it was a big sky and the likelihood of a midair collision, though a possibility, was much less likely than on the highway below, it was wise to keep my head on a swivel all the time.

Yuma slid by off to the left, and soon the lush Imperial Valley appeared below. The sharply delineated lines where the irrigation stops and the desert begins dramatically showed the miraculous effect of water on the desert floor. The ability of this comparatively small area to supply much of the nation's fresh vegetables in the winter season is almost magical. Indeed, the tiny community of Holtville, just east of the sprawling Naval Air Station at El Centro, is known as the Carrot Capitol of the world.

The coastal range of mountains known as the Lagunas lay dead ahead. Ronson casually scooped the microphone from its holder by his left hand and asked El Centro about the weather conditions in San Diego. As we had gained an hour of time by our westward movement, it was not yet noon.

El Centro advised that the morning coastal fog had dissipated and North Island Naval Air Station, our destination, was clear. As we reached the mountains, Ronson reached and retarded the throttles. Just as we began a gradual descent, the R4D began to ride like a wagon on a "washboard" road – bouncing and jouncing.

"The sea air hits the desert air about right here," Ronson explained. "The resulting turbulence can be a little disturbing to the passengers."

We slid through the jumpiness in a few minutes, and he said, "Better check on our hitchhiker. Tell her we'll be there in about 20 minutes."

I unbuckled my seatbelt and made my way back into the cabin. Our passenger was now awake, upright in the bucket seat with the seatbelt fastened. The jolting ride had apparently not caused any apprehension. On the contrary, she was obviously enjoying the flight as well as the scenery.

"Sorry about the bumps," I offered by way of an apology.

"Oh, I don't mind," she said. "I want to be a stewardess when the war's over, and this is good experience for me."

"We'll be in San Diego in a few minutes, so stay buckled up," I advised as I turned to go back to the front office.

I reported that our passenger had survived the choppy air and seemed to be enjoying the flight.

"She says she wants to be an airline stewardess."

"Yeah, I know," Ronson said. "A lot of 'em do. There will be a real need for them after the war. This is certainly the best way to move around the country and the sky's the limit. She'll do okay."

San Diego's unique water supply began to unfold as we held 255 degrees and continued our descent. Dams had been constructed at strategic locations in the mountain passes, creating large storage reservoirs.

The semi-arid coastal area was thus ensured a plentiful supply of the life-supporting fluid. The system, carefully designed over the last 100 years, was a masterpiece of hydro-geological engineering. Indeed, the design and construction had been a continuing process as the population of this delightful corner of the United States was growing rapidly.

Trees and chaparral gradually gave way to vineyards and citrus groves, and we called "NZY" (San Diego Naval Air Station) for landing clearance. I snapped the landing gear lever down and eased on 10 degrees of flaps. We passed south of the historic Hotel Del Coronado on final approach, and the wheels made a pleasant runch-runch sound as Ronson greased it on. We rolled up to the twin concrete hangars and pulled the mixture controls to idle cutoff.

As the propellers whined to a halt, I realized my first lesson in ferrying airplanes was over. Again I was reminded; Melvin had been right.

It *was* the cream of the duty.

Back in the saddle

It had been more than a month since I had flown a Corsair. My next flight, therefore, was labeled correctly in my logbook: "Familiarization." Two hours of simply flying around the winter landscape at Columbus was supposed to make me once again familiar with the airplane.

Ronson and I had been whisked back from the West Coast by the Navy's own Naval Air Transport Service. The R4D left San Diego at 6 p.m. local time and delivered us — after a long night in instrument conditions — to our home base the next morning. We touched down just as the sun began to make its way up into the gray winter sky.

In January, the Ohio scenery was devoid of color, consisting mostly of black and off-white with snow, now turned dirty gray from coal smoke, covering everything. Although the weather was technically clear, a persistent winter haze lay on the land and prevented the sun from warming the frigid air. Smoke curled from every chimney and factory smokestack and contributed to further reduction of the visibility.

Nonetheless I was, as always, elated to be back in the cockpit of my favorite airplane. Since I was to take a new Corsair to Alameda, California, the next day, the Chief Operations Officer had felt it might be a good idea for me to check out again before he entrusted me with a new one for delivery. Actually, this was accepted procedure. Flying, like swimming, is a permanently learned skill, but after a layoff its practitioners can become rusty. I found this to be true; but, with the seat height adjusted to my particular frame, I sat in the cockpit for a full half-hour, allowing my hands to refamiliarize themselves with every knob and lever within reach. This little informal agenda, quickly re-established my feel for the various relationships that familiarity with the airplane requires. My depth perception responses returned almost immediately. Soon I became one with the machine: a virtual extension of the control systems themselves.

Flaring the airplane for landing, taxiing around and through other parked airplanes, formation flying — all these functions must be performed with no conscious regard for distances between obstacles. One must be so familiar with his mount that safe relative movement in the immediate environment is automatic.

However, every pilot must guard against a trap: such a thorough acquaintance with a particular model airplane can develop a potentially deadly complacency unless one continuously guards against it. The Corsair was no exception. It required and demanded respect and performed superbly if treated with respect. With the slightest disregard of such consideration, however, the F4U — or any airplane — could turn on and bite its pilot.

Such thoughts were deliberately run through my head as I snapped the switches on and eased the mixture control into "automatic rich." The lineman had pulled the propeller through several times to redistribute the cold oil evenly throughout the 18 cylinders of the big Pratt & Whitney R-2800.

I called, "Clear," and hit the starter switch.

The battery, not at top efficiency because of the icy cold (23 degrees) day, slowly rotated the blades. With a couple of coughs and a few puffs of white exhaust, the engine burst into life.

Swirls of blue smoke curled over the wing. Sitting there waiting for the oil pressure to come up, I thought again that there is no other sound quite like that of a big radial aircraft engine. The arrangement of the cylinders in a circle, unlike those in a straight line (or two straight lines as in a V-8 or V-12 engine), changes the voice of a radial from the in-line engine's sound of a bunch of angry hornets to a deep, throaty roar.

I jerked my thumbs out, motioning for the wheel chocks to be pulled, and nudged the throttle a bit to break the tires loose from the grip of the ice. The big blue fighter rolled slowly toward the runway. Aligned for takeoff, I ran the manifold pressure up to about 38 inches and held my right foot firmly against the rudder pedal to counteract the torque of the powerful engine. As there was about a five- or six-knot breeze down the runway, I simply let my big blue bird fly itself off, then reached down and pulled the gear lever up and eased the throttle and propeller controls back to climb power: manifold pressure 34 inches, propeller 2,500 rpm, and climbing 1,500 feet a minute while moving along at 140 mph.

The sheer exhilaration of flight is difficult to describe. The thin air is certainly not man's natural element; perhaps this partially accounts for the deep satisfaction pilots feel as the slipstream flows smoothly past the contours of the wing and develops lift. If the love of flight is a disease, as some of the flight surgeons have (though perhaps facetiously) admitted, then I had it − bad.

At 8,000 feet, I topped the haze layer and broke out into a brilliant, clear sky of purest azure. Leveling off at 10,000 feet in the clear, cold sunlight of the winter day, I proceeded with my in-flight refamiliarization.

The quickest method to re-establish one's feel for an outstanding aerobatic airplane like the Corsair is to put it through an aerobatic routine, or "wring it out."

The routine I used started with slow rolls (also called aileron rolls since they are performed primarily by aileron movements) to the left and right. After these I pushed the nose down slightly, picked up about 200 knots, and eased the stick back. As we went up into a loop, I pushed the throttle to full power, backed off as we slid down the back side where gravity provided ample acceleration for the next maneuver.

Going right into the second loop, I watched as the horizon reappeared at the top of the loop, at which time I rolled the aircraft level completing an Immelmann turn — named for its originator in the German and French skies of World War I.

As the airspeed was now just above stalling speed, I performed half a snap roll to the left and, while thus inverted, pulled the nose into a vertical dive. The airspeed went by 200 knots promptly and I pulled into a loop once more. This time, however, as the top of the loop once again revealed the horizon, I did not roll upright until headed back down at about 30 degrees. Again picking up airspeed, I did the same thing again, thus joining two loops together into what is called a Cuban Eight, roughly a horizontal figure eight in the sky.

As I completed the second loop portion of the Cuban Eight, I allowed the airspeed to bleed off to 110 mph and snapped the stick straight back while pushing the left rudder to its limit. The resulting snap roll was perfect. This type of roll is actually a horizontal spin executed by deliberately snapping the aircraft into a stall at slow cruise speed in level flight, hence the terminology, "snap roll." The spin is stopped after 360 degrees of roll by adroit stick and rudder movements. I proceeded to do two more, to the left, then to the right, just for the fun of it.

After an hour of whirling around under the vault of the sky, it was time to return to earth. I descended reluctantly into the murk below, pleasantly fatigued by the exertion of performing aerobatics. The "g" forces sustained by both plane and pilot are substantial in such maneuvers and, although the airplane suffers not at all, the pilot's muscles react much the same as after a day's work at hard manual labor.

After a bit of probing about, I finally sorted out the airport from other snow-covered areas camouflaged by the low-altitude haze, and my refamiliarization ride ended with a smooth touch-down on the runway at Columbus. Turning off the strip, I parked the airplane in its designated spot, unhooked my seatbelt and earphone jack, and hefted my frame out of the cockpit. Standing in the retractable steps on the side of the fuselage, I closed the canopy and stepped stiff-legged to the ground. I saw my name posted opposite the notation: "FG1-D #76620 to NGU." (FG1-D was the Navy's designation for the F4U made by Goodyear in Akron.)

"Where is NGU?" I asked.

A voice behind me replied, "Alameda Naval Air Station in California. We leave in the morning."

I turned to greet my companion for the trip, my lead pilot, Jim Henderson, a Navy lieutenant (j.g.).

He smiled and his handshake was firm. The "fruit salad" decorating the left side of his blouse indicated he had had a successful tour in the South Pacific.

"Your first trip?" he asked.

"No," I responded. "Mr. Ronson and I took a new R4D to San Diego from Oklahoma City last week. Looks like we'll be covering some new territory."

"Yeah," he said. "We will turn northwest at El Centro, 120 miles east of San Diego, and fly up the San Joaquin Valley. Pretty this time of year."

His easy manner indicated it would be a pleasant trip, albeit an instructive one. Before new pilots assigned to the Ferry Squadron were allowed to go cross country alone, they were required to make at least two trips with lead pilots whose job would be to see that the neophyte ferry pilot didn't get lost. This had proved to be a wise procedure, since most pilots joining the squadron had done virtually all their flying within 100 miles of their training bases. After a few days' orientation, certain local landmarks became familiar and navigation as such became a redundant art. Also, the discipline imposed while in training precluded most straying from the immediate area around the training base. Occasionally a "lost" pilot would make an un-authorized "emergency" landing at an airport other than his home base, usually near his relatives' or his girlfriend's hometown. Such excursions, with their unfamiliar surroundings and procedures, too often met with disaster. Cadets, as well as new ensigns and second lieutenants, tended to overshoot small town airport runways, enter loops from 300 feet which usually resulted in a high-speed stall and spin as they ran out of altitude on the back side of the loop, plus the usual fuel starvation from misjudging distance and/or weather.

Consequently, on my first solo cross country in my new job, I was to be accompanied by a pathfinder.

"Did you pick up your maps yet?" Henderson asked.

"Yes, sir," I said, suddenly remembering my military protocol. "They're in my locker."

I went over to the row of small athletic room type lockers and pulled out a briefcase full of sectional aviation charts given to me at our original orientation lecture. Since I had already used them on the trip to San Diego, I had marked the course lines, distances, etc. for flights to the West Coast already, and I showed them to Henderson.

"Looks like you have done your homework," he said. He seemed relieved. He must have heard some of the stories about our predecessor Marine pilots in the ferry squadron concerning their disdain for proper navigation techniques with the resulting deviations from the stipulated ferry routes. I certainly planned no such waywardness, so I listened carefully as Henderson went over the route on the huge wall map of the United States that adorned the wall of our ready room.

Henderson was both conscientious and generous as he reiterat-ed the details of our route of flight, and for this I was grateful. I had heard some lead pilots greet their charges on the morning of the flight with a perfunctory, "Let's go. Just follow me."

He finished the session. "Any questions?"

"Yeah," I said. "Probably a lot of them, but you've been most helpful and I appreciate it."

He grinned and said, "Don't sweat it. See you in the morning. We'll get out of here about 0900 if the weather's okay."

After he left, I went out to the line and sought out the Corsair in which I would spend a good part of the next two or three days. After sitting in its cockpit for a few minutes, savoring the unique new airplane smells, I closed the canopy and jumped down to the frozen tarmac.

Arriving at the Squadron Operations Office the next morning a little after 8 a.m., I checked the weather along our route of flight and discovered that in some places it was somewhat marginal for visual flight. A warm front was moving up the Ohio River Valley from St. Louis, causing low ceilings and poor visibility over Indiana. However, conditions west of the Mississippi were reasonably clear.

Henderson strolled up to the Operations counter as I was filing my flight plan.

"How's it look to St. Louis?" he asked. He had heard about the front.

"Oh, we'll have some low stuff around Dayton to Terre Haute," I replied, "but apparently it is still VFR (Visual Flight Rules)."

Henderson went over to the Weather Information desk, behind which the teletype machines were clattering out the coded description of the latest weather along our course. By means of a series of symbols which, to the uninitiated, seem to be much the same as Egyptian hieroglyphics, meteorology stations across the country supplied us with a fairly accurate picture of the weather conditions affecting our line of flight. These bits of information relative to cloud cover, temperature, precipitation, and barometric pressure were updated each hour. Our decisions to fly or not to fly were made by interpreting that vitally important information. The predictions made by personnel in the Weather Offices, although certainly not infallible, were treated with great respect by all pilots.

Henderson nodded as he read the coded information, then picked up his flight bag and swung into his parachute harness. "Let's go."

As we taxied out for takeoff, the skies above looked anything but inviting, but the lateral visibility wasn't bad. I followed Henderson's Corsair as it took off into the haze and pulled up alongside his right wing tip as we banked smoothly off toward the southwest. We were able to skim along beneath the overcast at about 2,000 feet above the Ohio countryside so, as long as these conditions prevailed we should have no problems. To the south, the dark underside of the cumulus showed that it was obviously raining and, as we passed north of Dayton, we encountered a few rain showers but not enough to cause a serious reduction in visibility forward. As the temperature was at about 45 degrees, there was little danger of ice.

Henderson broke the silence in my earphones with, "Nice day. Is your airplane okay?"

"Just like they advertise," I said, trying to assure him that all was well.

It was, indeed, a superb machine, with its huge powerplant droning along at a slow cruise power setting, 25 inches of manifold pressure, 1,400 rpm, and 170 mph. What a pity its design and construction required the stimulation of war. The nation's survival, however, certainly justified its existence along with whatever talents we might inject into the maintenance of freedom on this cold winter day. Such thoughts seemed appropriate enough as we passed just south of the "Land of Lincoln" in Illinois.

The weather at St. Louis had improved by the time we arrived over the Mississippi, about two hours after takeoff. We were cleared to land at Lambert Field behind a United DC-3, which turned off to the passenger terminal while we proceeded to the Armed Forces parking area. The faces of the passengers in the airliner could be seen watching our gull-winged shapes with considerable curiosity, for the Corsair was still fairly new to the civilian environment and caused heads to turn wherever it appeared. They were probably wondering how such an ungainly looking contraption on the ground could be so fast in the air. These same thoughts, I was sure, had occurred to our wartime enemies in the Pacific.

As predicted, the weather toward Tulsa, Oklahoma, had improved; so, after a sandwich and a glass of milk in the field coffee shop in St. Louis, we filed for the Ozark leg of our journey.

The route we planned to follow is surely one of the most picturesque in the country: gentle rolling hills with no high mountains to "stuff the clouds full of rocks;" smooth meadows outlined by neat fence rows and roadways. Although not applicable this time of year, the area's nickname crossed my mind: "Tornado Alley." Every spring, awesome black funnels of swirling air wreak havoc upon this area, the result of a repetitive weather sequence with which all aviators who traverse this area are painfully familiar.

The meteorologists with whom I discussed the phenomenon had told me that our weather in the United States actually begins north of the Philippines, spawned in a continuous area of low pressure manufactured by the trade winds and heat just north of the equator in that part of the world. The resulting weather system proceeds northeast adjacent to Japan, passes south of the Aleutian chain, moves on southeast, and enters the United States at the Oregon and Washington coastline.

The series of fronts there begin their push across Idaho, Utah, Wyoming, and Colorado into the Panhandles of Texas and Oklahoma. There they are met by the warm moist air from the Gulf of Mexico, which causes them to spin, often violently, through Oklahoma, southern Missouri, and northern Arkansas while changing to a northeasterly movement. Thus carried along by their own momentum, they gradually meander up through the Ohio River Valley through West Virginia, Pennsylvania, and the New England states, finally dissipating off Nova Scotia. This process repeats itself about twice a week, more or less, and is fairly predictable.

Sometimes, though, a front would simply stop for a few days. (The meteorology people call these occluded fronts — we had other names for them.) Low ceilings and rain prevailed as ferry pilots depleted their supplies of underwear, shirts, and money while thus "grounded" by weather.

As we covered the two hours or so from St. Louis to Tulsa on that winter day, though, the skies were mostly clear. Passing Claremore, Oklahoma, about 15 minutes out, Henderson began a slow descent from our cruising altitude of 8,500 feet and shortly called the tower at Tulsa Municipal Airport.

After landing, we were directed to the military parking area, which that day was somewhat crowded with a group of Army Air Corps P-51 fighters that had just arrived out of New York. Only one parking space remained. Henderson and I looked at one another, then back at the smirking expressions on the faces of the Army pilots. We then calmly revealed the shipboard versatility of the Corsair by turning a small handle at our left sides whereupon the wings of our aircraft gently folded upward just outboard of the gull portion, thus allowing us to park both airplanes in a space normally required by one.

F4U with wings folded

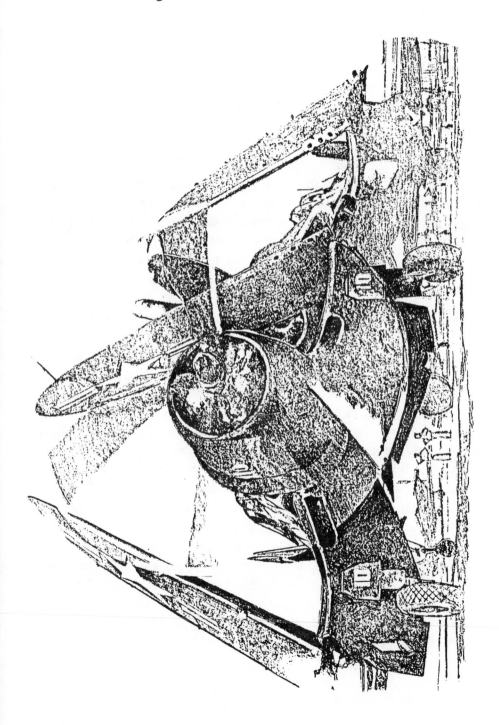

The civilian line personnel, some new to the job, simply stood with their hands on their hips shaking their heads in amazement. The folded wings further reduced our ground visibility from the cockpit, however, so we eased into the single space very carefully, pulling the mixture controls back into "idle cutoff." The propellers spun to a stop and we climbed down. The looks of utter disbelief on the faces of the dumbfounded Army pilots as we strolled smugly by them made our day.

Checking the weather toward Ft. Worth, our next stop, we found it to be more of the same with the exception of a few low clouds just past Ardmore over the Red River Valley. After topping the tanks with 100-octane, we climbed back into our saddles, fired up the engines, and – wings folded almost straight up – taxied past a gallery of waving schoolchildren lining the parking lot fence.

Like a couple of large geese, we unfolded our wings as the youngsters watched in amazement. I couldn't help wondering how they would describe this portion of their visit when their teacher collected their written reports on "A Day at the Airport."

The predicted clouds appeared on schedule but proved to be no problem as the bases were about 4,000 feet above the East Texas landscape. We were flying in a comfortable formation, about 400 feet apart, with Henderson from time to time pointing out various landmarks that he knew would be of future assistance to me when I was on the route alone – a certain bend in a river here, a double-track railroad there, a town with a water tank and a racetrack. The oval shape of this latter addition to the usual checkerboard pattern of a town makes is an easy-to-spot navigational aid. By checking the location of the racetrack relative to the town itself with the location on one's map of the area, positive identification is easy. Such knowledge is useful in times of low visibility and wavering fuel gauges.

The aroma of Ft. Worth stockyards soon announced our arrival. Since the wind was from the south, we requested a "straight in" approach to Meacham Field.

I dropped back behind Henderson, lowered the wheels and flaps, and followed him down. Since it was now past three o'clock in the afternoon, we helped the lineman bed down the two Corsairs for the night and strolled over to check in with the FCLO, a Navy lieutenant.

"We probably could have gone on to Midland today, but this is a $7.00 stop and Midland is a $3.00 stop. You know the difference?" Henderson inquired.

"No, but I guess I'm about to learn," I replied.

Night ferry flights were, along with instrument flights, taboo in the Ferry Squadrons. It was mandatory that we land and have our aircraft parked before official sunset each day.

The monetary nomenclature stemmed from the Navy's procedure in making arrangements for our night's stay at various stops along our usual routes around the country. Where government quarters were available, as was the case at the Army Air Corps Base at Midland, Texas, we were paid $3.00 along with our flight pay and thus our extra lodging expense while "enroute in line of duty" was reimbursed.

However, if government quarters were not available at our day's end destination, the overnight stipend was a munificent $7.00! This increase was provided to pay the additional expenses made necessary because of our having to find respite from our day's arduous duties in various civilian hotels, restaurants, night clubs, and other places of rest and recreation. As could be imagined, $7.00 was a far cry from the actual expenses incurred, but the more adventuresome pilots could generally always find a $7.00 stop before sunset. Ergo, Ft. Worth, as a $7.00 stop in ferry pilot parlance, was considered a more desirable place to RON (remain overnight) than a mere $3.00 stop.

We boarded the airport bus with some of our ferry pilot cohorts and proceeded to the Blackstone Hotel, where the Navy continually reserved rooms for itinerant pilots. After an evening of congenial hyperbole with others of our specialty, I hit the sack. It had been an uneventful but informative day. I was learning the trade.

I awoke to the jangling 0600 wake-up call to see a gray overcast. On the telephone, the rainmaker cheerfully said that the weather west would be flyable shortly although at that moment it was instrument conditions, so we took on some breakfast in the hotel coffee shop and caught the first bus to the airport.

As I walked from the bus to the Operations Office to file our flight plan to El Paso, I caught sight of a familiar loose-jointed, six-foot, four-inch, skinny Marine pilot trying to decipher the weather sequence just being printed on the teletype. It was Bill Decker, whom I hadn't seen since Basic Training at Corpus Christi.

After the usual good-natured insults about his inability to read the weather data, he responded with mock amazement at my capacity to remain alive in the flying business. We brought each other up to date on our own activities as well as the usual "Whatever happened to old so-and-so?" Such enjoyable camaraderie was, of course, standard in military circles. Good friendships were formed, though only a few were very deep and lasting. We learned to depend on one another, but in wartime the subconscious nagging fear of losing friends made us reluctant in their firm acquisition.

I introduced Decker to Henderson, who kiddingly alluded to Decker's towering frame.

"They're building Marines pretty tall these days," he said. Henderson, at about five feet, seven inches, certainly was obliged to look up to Decker.

After the expected friendly banter about the relative merits of the Navy and Marine Corps, Henderson asked, "What're you flyin'?"

"I've got that General Motors Turkey out there for San Diego, out of New York," he said. "I guess I came in after you two landed yesterday."

The term "Turkey," as applied to the famous Grumman torpedo bomber, the TBF Avenger, was not a derisive term but one of description. The torpedo bay ended abruptly aft of the cockpit enclosure, on the underside of the aircraft, and the empennage looked as it if had been added as an afterthought. The whole affair gave the visual impression of a large bird. It was larger than the Corsair, though considerably slower, and had no trouble lifting off from a carrier with a deadly torpedo tucked in its belly.

"Today I've got a load of hitchhikers, so it should be a fun trip," Decker said, grinning.

Four Navy hospital Corpsmen were going to sandwich themselves in various cubbyholes in the big Grumman and freeload to the West Coast, thus saving their travel money provided by the Navy.

We went through preflight inspections, including checking the movement of the controls, and completed the thorough gyrations of strapping on the parachutes, which had remained in the aircraft overnight. There were no provisions for luggage in the Corsair, since it was designed for fighting rather than travel. Various spots had been tried for storing ferry pilots' personal effects, and under the seat seemed to be the best place, so we fitted our green zipper bags into that niche. Although our bags rested on the

69

round metal control shaft extending under the seat back to the elevator, they did not inhibit its movement, so as far as we could see it was a perfectly safe procedure.

The overcast began to develop a few holes about 0930, so we departed Ft. Worth for El Paso and punched up through one of the holes to fly on top. By the time we reached Mineral Wells, 40 miles to the west, the clouds had dissipated. The temperature was about 35 degrees, but the sun shining through the clear plexiglass canopy warmed the cockpit nicely. Henderson was off to my left about a quarter of a mile; I edged in a little closer so there was no possibility of our losing sight of one another.

Within a half-hour, we saw that our flight of two was overtaking another airplane dead ahead at our same altitude, 10,500 feet. From the thickset appearance, we knew that it was Decker's Turkey.

Sneakily, Henderson and I throttled back and pulled up alongside of Decker before, with an enormous doubletake, he became aware of our tight formation presence off each wing. He had the big "fish carrier" on automatic pilot and was absorbed in a book! His passengers were goggle-eyed at seeing two other airplanes flying so closely, our wings edging under their airplane's wingtips. For several minutes they waved nervously to us as we flew alongside, then Decker picked up his microphone and said, "Go away, you guys. I'm resting."

The Turkey's cockpit was spacious and comfortable, even though its designed function provided little comfort for the enemy's navy. We tossed Decker and the corpsmen a salute, peeled off, and, resetting our throttles and propellers to cruise position, we pulled away rapidly from the plodding TBF.

Just east of Big Spring, Henderson and I were tooling along, about a hundred yards apart, enjoying the West Texas scenery from our comfortable vantage point two miles up.

CHARLES CORDELL

From over my left shoulder, I caught a fleeting glint of sunlight reflecting from two meteor-like objects that almost instantly hurtled downward directly between our two Corsairs, so close that their resulting slipstream caused a slight shudder in my airplane. They were gone in a flash, but I recognized the aircraft that had bounced us as two Army Air Corps "Jugs" — P-47 fighters from the Fighter Training Base at Big Spring. Henderson keyed his microphone.

"Shall we put in for combat pay?" he asked, with a grin in his voice — all fighter pilots are ready to accept such a challenge.

"Might be hard to prove to the pay clerk," was my guarded response, although I had my hand on the throttle ready to follow my leader.

Such ad hoc activities by young fighter pilots were certainly neither condoned nor encouraged by any official training syllabus in any branch of the Armed Forces, but youthful exuberance being what it is, the intra-fraternal rivalry between Army and Naval fighter pilots made such airborne shenanigans almost routine.

Here were two pairs of young men (probably 21 or 22 years of age) at the peak of their combat training, having become truly proficient at aerial gunnery, rocketry, skip bombing, and now masters of the piloting skills necessary to carry out these deadly activities. They were ready, having been thoroughly indoctrinated by their instructors with the best fighter airplane training and mounted in the most sophisticated pieces of combat aviation equipment ever built; they were literally itching to try it.

So when two teams of peers in similar aircraft but from a rival branches of the Armed Forces — Jugs on high spotting Corsairs cruising far below in the morning serenity of the West Texas atmosphere — not a word was uttered by the two Jug pilots as the engagement took shape in their minds.

Their control columns were moved deftly to the left and forward as they picked up almost terminal velocity and went screaming down to attack out of the sun, in the classic hit-and-run attack. Were we actually the enemy, their arrays of 50-caliber machine guns (identical to our own) could have obliterated us before we were even aware of their presence. They knew that we had no chance to get their numbers and, even if we could have, we wouldn't have dreamed of reporting them. They expected us to dive with them, but Henderson — who had engaged in the real thing not long before, suggested that we would simply wait our chance another day. As we were their exact counterparts, the same competitive urges motivated us as well, but since our mounts were to be delivered to the Fleet in mint condition, discretion prevented our acceptance of the challenge.

After the Jug bounce, we progressed toward the big sand pile near Wink, Texas. About 20 miles wide, its desolate surface conjured up all manner of evil foreboding about possible engine failure, stumbling through the sand with no water, with our bleached bones ultimately being found by hunters. My imagination could almost envision the scene below as it must have looked 50 million years before, with dinosaurs and other early inhabitants of the Permian Basin foraging about the desolate landscape below. No pterodactyls attempted to join our formation, however, and our new engines maintained their steady drone.

Henderson and I departed El Paso a little past noon and were pleasantly surprised as Deming, New Mexico, slid by ahead of schedule to the north, indicating that the usual prevailing westerly wind was absent that day. According to my dead reckoning computer, we would arrive at the Naval Auxiliary Air Station at Thermal, California, in a little over three hours. We passed along the eastern edge of the Salton Sea, that 30-mile-long inland sea formed when the Colorado River overflowed its banks in 1905, and called the Thermal tower at about 2 p.m., having picked up an extra hour's daylight by moving into the Pacific Time Zone.

Landing at Thermal, we were fitted into eight F6F Hellcat fighters doing "bounce drill" — simulated carrier approaches and landings — in the traffic pattern. This operation accustomed Navy pilots to procedures they would use in actually landing aboard a ship under way at sea. I immediately remembered Mr. Flournoy's similar indoctrination of our flight at Green Cove Springs.

Simulating carrier approaches over the California desert, where the temperature ran about 90 degrees, was an interesting experience in that aircraft fly the curved final approach at just above stalling speed. Carrier landings are made in a small area, hence such flying must be precise. If one encountered a rising column of air (for which this community was named) as he approached the throttle "cut" position over the runway threshold, the resulting aerodynamic gyrations could be hair-raising indeed. To maintain — or regain — control during the sudden burst of lift from the rising column of air, and the subsequent drop when the plane flew through it, required all the skill a pilot could muster.

At sea, a pilot's main concern when landing is the fantail of the carrier's flight deck rising in a heavy sea while his airplane is coming down. The resulting "ca-runch!" can keep the mechanics on the hangar deck busy for days, not to mention the hours the medics spend trying to put one's vertebrae and fillings back where they belong.

We were sandwiched into the pattern by the cooperative tower personnel, then landed and taxied up to the service ramp for fuel. Several F6F Hellcats were parked nearby. Henderson and I ambled over to inspect the Corsair's latest companion in the Fleet. Its F4F Wildcat ancestry was readily apparent with the deep round fuselage and squared-off wing and tail surfaces.

There the similarity ended. The full-chested Hellcat was much larger, though more maneuverable, than the Wildcat. The wheels retracted into the wings rather than into the fuselage, giving it a much wider tread, thus eliminating the built-in ground loop tendency of the smaller F4F. Its engine was the same R-2800 as in the Corsair, so the two aircraft were almost identical in performance, with the Corsair allegedly being a little bit faster. (This latter allegation would be disputed by all Hellcat pilots!)

It did have one built-in characteristic, however, that made it the ideal carrier fighter. At landing air speed, about 67 knots, the attitude of the Hellcat was at the three-point position. This made hooking the first arresting wire on the carrier deck much easier than was the case with the Corsair, which actually stalls before reaching the three-point position. The Corsair pilot, therefore, had to make a conscious effort to snap the tail down and catch the wire with the tail hook as the airplane literally fell to the deck. In heavy seas, this could be a memorable experience and, if the resulting "bang!" was too severe, the Corsair would break in two just aft of the cockpit.

We enjoyed several minutes' discussion with the F6F pilots about their machines while our Corsairs' tanks were filled, and then departed Thermal. Taking off to the south, Henderson and I banked around and tucked in tight. We came back across the field "full bore" just to show the Hellcats' pilots how a real airplane could move out! We then headed northwest on the final 475 miles to Alameda.

Both San Jacinto and San Gorgonio Peaks, at 10,805 and 11,485 feet, respectively, were adorned with their winter mantle of white as we climbed to our cruising altitude of 10,500 feet. Passing these two sentinels to the Banning Pass, with the afternoon sun's rays beginning to break up into the colors of the spectrum as they hit the snow, provided some of Mother Nature's most spectacular vistas.

Henderson finally broke the silence. "Pretty, huh?"

Quickly, I agreed with him. I was also thankful we weren't here when all that snow was being deposited. Southern California's storms are noted for their fury, and a flight through such weather can be violently terminated.

Today, however, the forecast given to us at Thermal for clear skies and a modest headwind held true and we passed Bakersfield right on our projected time. Fresno soon passed us on the right as we banked left toward Stockton. San Francisco Bay appeared shortly thereafter, with the city's fantastic skyline silhouetted against the late afternoon sun; truly a "golden gate."

We touched down at Alameda a few minutes before official sunset, so we were legal. Even one minute after sunset made us "flying during the hours of darkness" which was "verboten" as has been previously noted, in the ferry pilot's rule book.

Henderson showed me how to sign off the airplane with the yeoman in charge at the flight office. We were then driven over to the Transient Officers' Quarters, where we were assigned our sleeping facilities. Dinner at the Officers' Club was reasonably priced and delicious. Afterward, some of our compatriots went across the bay to San Francisco, where they proceeded to build themselves some memories until the wee hours of the morning.

I retired early to my room, where the phone rang as I started to recap the day's activities.

It was Henderson. He was calling to inform me that orders had been posted for him to take an SNJ single-engine training plane to Bremerton, Washington, the next day, and for me to return to Columbus via commercial airlines.

"What's the procedure for tickets?" I asked.

"No problem," Henderson said. "The Disbursing Office will give you a transportation request. We call them T/R's." Henderson had been issued his own T/R book authorizing him to obtain passage for himself and any other pilots under his supervision on any domestic airline to any point in the country. Reflecting the importance of ferrying aircraft, such requests bore a mandatory "War B Priority." Once the T/R was presented, the airline clerk was obliged to implement it on the first flight available on penalty of dismissal. This latter feature could have some amusing implications, particularly when a passenger agent bumped previously booked passengers from their seats. I will never forget the look of utter frustration and cold fury on the face of an admiral, when an airline clerk told him he would have to relinquish his seat to me, a ferry pilot, and take the next flight. It was an unusual position, especially when the ferry pilot was a Marine second lieutenant.

"All you do is take the T/R to the airline counter at Oakland Airport in the morning. They'll book you right through to Columbus. Do you have a bag for your parachute?"

"Yeah," I said. "I can manage. And thanks for your help, checking me out in this operation."

"Oh, you'll do okay," Henderson said. "I'm recommending you for lead pilot when I get back to the squadron. So don't make a liar out of me next trip."

This was surprising news. I thanked him again for "Henderson's Helpful Hints," which made it possible. Being a lead pilot meant I was qualified to go anywhere in the country alone, so I wouldn't have to wait for the availability of a lead pilot each time I was assigned to a trip.

The transition from fighter pilot to ferry pilot was apparently complete.

Lemon delivery

Actually, there had been ample warning. The thin film of oil now coating the windshield of the big Corsair fighter started to appear soon after takeoff. Since the aircraft was brand-new, I didn't give it much thought. The aircraft logbook showed the usual "four hours," which was the time required for the inflight pilots to bring the plane down from Akron where it was built, to Columbus, plus some "run-in" time. After all, this was the latest example of fighter-plane technology, and the craftsmanship of the factory personnel who produced it was well known. In addition, the "run-in" check pilots were supposed to ferret out any "bugs" in the airplane, so it would be made service-ready for the Fleet. Still, the oil film was there and, by the time I reached Terre Haute, it was heavy enough to make forward visibility difficult.

The weather in the middle of the Midwest winter was numbingly cold. The past week's snowstorm in the Ohio River Valley was still making the bleak landscape below reflect the bitterness of the worst winter in 52 years. It was February 1945, and the weather seemed to reflect the wartime atmosphere that pervaded our nation and the world.

Henderson had apparently filed his report, since I was now considered by someone to be sufficiently indoctrinated to find my way to California alone. Thus, my assignment that cold February morning: Deliver FG-1D aircraft #88636 to "NGU" (Alameda, California, Naval Air Station). I was not so sure.

The officially approved ferry route to California from Columbus, Ohio, followed a series of established airways charted for navigation in the civilian system by a number and color code. The particular airway from Columbus to St. Louis was designated as "Green Four." From St. Louis it veered southwest to Tulsa and Ft. Worth, as "Amber Four," then continued on to San Diego as "Green Five." This routing along the southern part of the country was on the assumption that the usual winter weather would be somewhat less harsh than on a more northerly route to the West Coast. Pilots soon learned that this assumption was not necessarily accurate, but it was certainly considered logical by those people back in headquarters who were charged with making such decisions.

From Ft. Worth the next stop was Midland or El Paso, depending on the amount of headwind one encountered. El Paso was almost at the end of the normal non-stop ferry range of the Corsair, which was about three and one-half hours from Ft. Worth. Consequently, it was usually prudent to stop at Midland for fuel before proceeding farther west.

Some of my squadron mates had learned this by what had become known as the "Salt Flat Detour." El Paso, with its proximity to Juarez, Mexico, right across the border, had a very powerful attraction as an RON stop. Consequently, there was a tendency for some of my more adventuresome compatriots to "extend the range" of the Corsair to make El Paso the first day out of Columbus, rather than Midland. On several occasions, the headwinds encountered in West Texas had consumed all the fuel in Corsairs whose unfortunate pilots had to put them down on the highway at Salt Flat, Texas, approximately 75 miles east of El Paso. This was not too difficult to do, but subjected an unwary pilot to endless jibes by his peers, plus the mountain of reports he was required to complete, even the possibility of a court martial.

One such unfortunate pilot, upon landing on the road (almost deserted in wartime), found that his engine would restart and decided he would continue. He took off, whereupon the remaining fuel, which had drained to the back of the tank as the airplane assumed the three-point position on landing, now resumed a forward position as the aircraft reached level flight. The resulting engine failure on takeoff necessitated putting the aircraft down in rough terrain. Although the pilot was uninjured, his pride (and his career) suffered considerably. At last report, he was permanently assigned as duty officer at the Marine detachment on Ascension Island.

From El Paso, Green Five continued to Deming, New Mexico, which was usually bypassed, and on to Coolidge, Arizona, a small community just south of Phoenix. Although the air base at Coolidge was large and amply equipped, it was almost perfectly camouflaged by its desert surroundings as one approached it from the southeast. New pilots along the route almost invariably flew right by it without seeing it and wound up at one of the Army training bases around Phoenix, suffering from acute fuel shortage. Most soon discovered, as I did, that if one went right over a small mountain peak that juts rather prominently from the desert floor about 20 miles south of Coolidge Airport and held a steady northwesterly course, the airport appeared over the nose in about five or six minutes.

Coolidge to San Diego was usually an easy one hour and 40 minute flight, but it was prudent to check San Diego's weather as one passed the Naval Air Station at El Centro, California. The coastal city of San Diego was noted for its delightful year-round climate, but its unique pattern of night and morning low clouds and fog, although constituting a sort of "built-in" air-conditioning system for the city, didn't make for ideal runway approach and landing conditions. Occasionally in the spring one could depart Coolidge for San Diego with the weather reported as "clearing soon," only to discover when checking an hour or so later at El Centro that it was still "clearing soon," but not yet.

As I had learned during my previous delivery with Henderson, when the terminus of ferry flights was Alameda, California, rather than San Diego, a turn to the northwest onto another airway was made at El Centro. One then continued on over the mountains at Palm Springs, through the lush San Joaquin Valley and the pass south of Stockton "under the weather" to Oakland and on to the adjacent Naval Air Station at Alameda on San Francisco Bay's east side.

It should be reiterated that all ferry flights were required to be conducted "VFR" (Visual Flight Rules). Although instrument flight through adverse weather was performed routinely by the airlines and our aircraft were similarly equipped, only a very few ferry pilots had the time and experience, the Navy reasoned, to be permitted to conduct ferry flights "on the gauges." This was probably a wise ruling, as we were all fresh out of Flight School and certainly had not used our instrument training to any great extent. The spatial disorientation in clouds, if one was not accustomed to regular instrument flight, could be disastrous, particularly if those clouds concealed large chunks of granite, as they often did.

* * *

Except for the oil film, the airplane — my first solo delivery — seemed to be operating perfectly. Even the cockpit heater worked reasonably well. Most fighter cockpits were noted for their austerity, but this airplane was roomy and comfortable. The outside air at my cruising altitude of 6,500 feet was 18 degrees, but inside the enclosed cockpit the thermometer hung on about 50. So, with all the heavy winter flight gear the Navy issued to each Marine pilot covering my Southern-born frame, I was snug and warm.

The airspeed indicator read 180 mph, little less than half the speed of which the Corsair was capable. Our instructions were to take it easy during ferry flights so the aircraft would be in top condition when it joined the Fleet. Its big 18-cylinder radial engine purred contentedly at 1,300 rpm. Its 2,000 horses were reined back to less than half that at this power setting.

I could almost count the blades of the propeller turning at only 650 rpm, being geared down to a two-to-one ratio with the engine revolutions. Its three blades measured thirteen and one-half feet in diameter, which was monstrous for a fighter plane but necessary to absorb the tremendous power of the new twin-row Wasp engine. The huge propeller also accounted for another design phenomenon: an inverted gull wing that allowed a landing gear assembly short enough to retract while affording sufficient propeller clearance when extended. Even so, the whole wheel assembly was enormously complicated, turning 90 degrees as the gear came up into the wings. The appearance of the aircraft on the ground, therefore, was that of an ugly duckling, but the contours in the air, with wheels tucked smoothly into the wings, gave not only the vision of speed but the reality as well.

Yet, there was that nagging oil on the windshield. It was not the black gushing stream of oil depicted in the B-movie version of a failing aircraft engine, but simply a clear persistently thickening film that distorted and ultimately blocked effective vision forward. I decided that I'd have it checked at St. Louis when I stopped for fuel.

Vandalia and Greenville, Illinois, slipped beneath the wings, and I began to prepare for landing at St. Louis. Lateral visibility on this winter morning was about 15 miles, so I soon picked up East St. Louis and the Mississippi River out of the left side of the cockpit. The oil film had not yet entirely coated the side windows, so vision in this direction was not totally impaired. Landing should not be a problem since Navy regulations required landing with the bubble canopy open all the way. My plan was to make a normal downwind approach, line up with the runway, and gauge my touchdown by leaning out the side of the windshield.

As I crossed the "Big Muddy" over East St. Louis, I called Lambert Field for landing instructions, having decided not to tell the tower personnel of my problem with the oil leak; I was concerned that they might declare an emergency, which would put the field on full alert, complete with fire engines and ambulance along the runway's edge, and closing the airport to all normal operations. Also, it would be necessary to go to the Civilian Operations Office and fill out endless forms, carefully explaining the "emergency." So I elected to enter the landing pattern routinely and, by making a circular, carrier-type approach, with my head out of the side of the cockpit until almost the moment of touchdown, the landing was completely uneventful.

I taxied over to the Navy facility, shut down the engine, and crawled out, wiping my hand on the oil-coated windshield. As the Navy fuel truck pulled up, I was already examining the front of the engine cowling and propeller hub to see if I could find the source of the oil. It was apparently a minor leak in the propeller hub assembly, which fact I pointed out to the line mechanic.

He looked up at me and, with only slightly concealed disdain, said, "Aw, Lieutenant, it's probably just a gasket that hasn't seated properly yet. We'll clean it off and you can go on to Tulsa and see if it doesn't quit leaking."

Feeling that the rated mechanic was probably correct, I concurred in his offhand diagnosis and signed for the 118 gallons of fuel and two gallons of oil. Then I went over to the Operations Office and filed a flight plan for Tulsa, Oklahoma.

Tulsa was about two hours from St. Louis. By the time I reached Springfield, Missouri — the halfway point — the oil film was back again exactly as before it had been cleaned, but I continued on, hoping the "unseated gasket" would eventually find its proper slot and stop the leak. The landing at Tulsa was again head-out-of-the-side routine and the line personnel voiced the same opinion as their colleagues at St. Louis.

"It's okay, sir," one of the mechanics told me when I returned from a quick lunch, "a lot of these new props do that."

Somewhat assured, I fired up the big round engine and departed for Ft. Worth. The oil immediately began to coat the windshield, and I seriously considered turning back toward Tulsa. The prospect of the long flight into the western sun with its rays diffused by an oily windshield was not pleasant. However, the flight to Ft. Worth was only about an hour and a half, so I rationalized that I'd be that much farther along. I also remembered that the Navy maintained a complete repair shop at its facility in Ft. Worth, so I was confident the personnel there could remedy the sticky situation. And, although this particular airplane was destined for Alameda rather than San Diego, I might be able to complete the delivery the next day. I would insist that the propeller gasket be replaced tonight.

My approach to Meacham Field at Ft. Worth took me right over the stockyards north of the city so it was easy to understand how the city got its nickname, "Cowtown." Thousands of beef cattle passed through on the way to the markets of the world from these yards. On warmer days, with the humidity and wind conditions just right, the distinct odor (Texans called it the "smell of money") constituted a sort of "olfactory approach beacon" to the airport, immediately south of the cattle pens.

The wheels rolled smoothly on the blacktop as I once again taxied into the ramp area with my head out the side of the open canopy so I could see. Visibility over the thirteen feet of nose in the Corsair was, at best, rather limited on the ground. And with the oil film streaking the windshield, taxiing was something of an adventure.

Eventually I managed to get the airplane parked and pointed out the oil problem to the line chief. He agreed that it should be fixed before proceeding on to the West Coast, so I would write the problem on the Navy's infamous "yellow sheet" (a maintenance "gripe sheet" on which pilots were required to cite the various malfunctions of the aircraft, if any, after each flight). Then I walked over to the Operations Office to make arrangements for overnight lodging.

I dialed one of the posted hotel numbers at the Operations desk and made reservations for the night. Then I settled down to the task of describing on my aircraft's yellow sheet the discrepancy of the propeller oil seal. As the aircraft was new, there was no possibility of the malfunction being due to some error on my part, and for this I was very grateful. Lapses in efficiency on the part

85

of trained Navy personnel that resulted in damage to Naval property usually required appearance before Commanding Officers, Review Boards, and others of like ilk. At such times, logical explanations of the culprit's malfeasance in line of duty had to be forthcoming or the results could be devastating to one's morale, particularly to one's "hip pocket morale."

My evening meal at the hotel more than compensated for the peanut butter and jelly sandwich luncheon and the bed was comfortable, so when the 5:30 a.m. call came, I awoke properly rejuvenated for the remaining journey.

The crew in the shop had replaced the malfunctioning oil seal in the propeller hub during the night and an entry in the plane's engine log read: "Improper seal installed at factory. Correct seal installed this date."

After filing a flight plan for El Paso, I climbed aboard, lit off the engine, and taxied out for takeoff as the sun's rays angled across the skyline of downtown Ft. Worth. There was a nice breeze blowing from the southeast, so I eased the throttle forward until the manifold pressure showed only about two-thirds rated power. We lifted effortlessly into the crisp morning air, turned right, and took up a westerly heading across the barren winter landscape of central Texas.

I noted with great relief that the windshield remained free of oil. The usual headwind was absent, so Midland was bypassed as the fuel gauges showed El Paso would be within range with a small reserve. The course took me south of Guadalupe Peak which, at 8,751 feet, is the highest point in Texas. It is the southernmost "last hurrah" of the Rocky Mountain chain as this massive backbone of North America subsides into the plains of western Texas.

I detoured slightly and flew for a few minutes around the huge stone outcroppings at the top of the mysterious looking mountain. I was surprised to see several houses meshed into the landscape, along with some trees, gardens, and other evidence of an ever-expanding human population. Although a road could be seen criss-crossing its way down the mountain, I was struck by the isolation of the community. Truly, the American pioneer spirit was alive and well. Such musings ceased as I rolled the wheels at El Paso, grabbed a sandwich and a glass of milk at the terminal building cafe and, after checking the propeller hub and finding no leaks, headed for Coolidge, Arizona.

Situated about 15 minutes west of El Paso is an unusual bit of geographic phenomena. Apparently several hundred thousand years ago, this particular spot was the target of a massive chunk of debris from outer space which, after its cataclysmic "Ker-thunk!" into the earth, left quite a large hole in the ground. There now appeared to be a couple of fair-sized farms down in it. As I droned overhead, the Kilbourne Hole, as it is known, was a visual reminder that creation is a continuing process and can be rather violent at times.

I was learning the hard way that the human anatomy is not designed to withstand the "long sit." I had heard of instances where pilots actually acquired bed-sores on the buttocks because of the continual pressure against the parachute pack, inflatable dinghy, first aid kit, and canteen, which comprised the seat cushions in all military single-engine aircraft. In addition, the inactivity sustained by a pilot's lower torso interfered with the normal cycle of elimination. We all had been told early in our tours as ferry pilots to continue performing the hated calisthenics to which we had been subjected regularly as cadets. If we didn't function regularly, we were subject to discomfort, painfully manifested in varying degrees of "mucous colitis" and other malfunctions of the lower digestive tract. Pilots soon learned to forego bread and potatoes for fruit and vegetables if they wanted to remain on the flight roster. It was actually possible to distinguish the transport and other multi-engine pilots from us single-engine types by the measure of their girth and their propensity for using back or chest-type parachutes.

The Corsair had no floor under the seat, but rather two narrow platforms running fore and aft of the rudder pedals upon which we rested our heels while we positioned our toes on the pedals. One benefit was that those of us who regularly flew that airplane could achieve a measure of relief by unbuckling our seatbelt and parachute harness and standing partially erect in the cockpit to relieve the pressure for a time.

Such deviations from regulations could produce exciting results. On one solo ferry trip while "unhooked" from the airplane's seat, I accidentally dropped my sunglasses to the very bottom of the cockpit area. They could be seen resting unbroken on the aluminum skin of the fuselage. I decided to "scrunch" down and see if I cold retrieve them. Carefully leveling the Corsair at 8,500 feet, I began the contortions required to reach the glasses, momentarily taking my eyes off the artificial horizon instrument.

In mid-scrunch, my shoulder nudged the control column to the left and forward, putting the sensitive fighter into a screeching diving left turn. Any ideas of recapturing the errant sunglasses were immediately forgotten while I essayed a recovery from the spiral dive by using my left hand on the stick and simultaneously pushing the right rudder with my right hand. Finally, after thirty seconds, which seemed an eternity, the airplane regained some semblance of level flight and I carefully eased back into my seat, hooked up all the harnesses, and brought the airplane back on course while my heartbeat slowly returned almost to normal. The residents of northeastern Texas, where this occurred, probably talked for months about the wild gyrations of the "Navy fighter plane out of control."

* * *

Shortly after three in the afternoon, Coolidge appeared in its desert camouflage. I elected to RON at this remote $3.00 stop. The "available government quarters" consisted of the usual austere barracks, but the beds were comfortable and the food at the Mess Hall was of gourmet quality. I was in good spirits as the aircraft had performed perfectly with no further trouble with ill-fitting or improper gaskets.

Leaving Coolidge with the morning sun at my back, I was struck by the singular winter beauty of the Arizona desert. The sun was far south and cast a pleasant glow over the stark countryside. I remained below 500 feet for a while and was fascinated by the amount of vegetation on the desert floor. Marvelously designed by nature to withstand the blistering heat of summer and the frigid stillness of winter, the huge saguaro cactus, chollas, mesquite, and ocotillo would soon be adorned with the brilliant desert flowers for which this part of the world is famous.

I was also reminded of the difference between most of the rivers of the great Southwest and their Eastern counterparts. Green Five Airway followed the Gila River Valley into Yuma, Arizona, but there was very little, if any, water in the river. It was there, to be sure, a few feet below the desert surface, but only during periods of heavy rain did the water manifest itself in sufficient quantity to make a real river. At such times, the cities along the Gila learned the uses of sandbags, levees, and bulldozers in their efforts to contain the rampaging waters. Gradually, a system of dams was being built to keep the flood damage at a minimum while, at the same time, making irrigation of the fertile desert possible. The resulting agricultural production was astounding.

Crossing the mighty Colorado River at Yuma, I entered the Golden State, where a surprising geological formation soon appeared below. The huge sandbox of southeastern California running about 40 miles in a northwesterly direction from Yuma to the Salton Sea looked exactly like the sand dunes of the Sahara. At such times, one had a tendency to imagine small extraneous noises in the engine compartment, noises that disappeared magically as soon as the forbidding terrain below slipped behind me.

El Centro called for a right turn for the fuel stop at Thermal, California, where I enjoyed a delicious date shake with my lunch. The Naval Air Station at Thermal was situated in the middle of a grove of giant date palm trees, so the galley crews had learned to formulate some rather exotic concoctions from the local products.

With both aircraft and pilot refueled, I climbed from below sea level at Thermal to 10,500 feet and headed northwest for Bakersfield, in the San Joaquin Valley. The ground fog that usually covered most of this broad central California valley had burned off by the time I crossed the Tehachapis. It was easy to see why this area was known the world over for its agricultural production. A broad flat valley extending some 250 miles from the Sacramento Delta area to the Tehachapi Mountains, lying between the coastal range of mountains and the Sierra Nevada, it was uniquely suited for truck crops of every kind. Its wine grape production rivaled that of France and Spain.

Turning westerly at Modesto, I passed south of Stockton and soon called the Navy tower at Alameda for landing instructions. The sun was now well past its zenith for the day and, as usual, the wind was from the west, placing the bright sunlight in my eyes as I turned on final approach. I had already moved the landing gear lever to the "down" position, and I reached up for the flap handle to extend my air brakes for landing. They extended only about 20 degrees . . . and stopped.

I recycled the handle. This time the air brakes didn't even reach 20 degrees. At this point, the landing gear extension indicator caught my eye and I noted that the left main gear was fully extended but its companion on the right was only halfway down, certainly an abnormal landing configuration.

A quick look at the hydraulic fluid pressure gauge showed its normal thousand-pound reading to be precisely zero. A glance out the window at the trailing edge of the wing showed the last few drops of reddish hydraulic fluid, the life blood of most of the systems on this airplane, vanishing in the slipstream.

Immediately I applied power and pulled up and out of the traffic pattern, while advising the tower of my predicament. I informed them that I would try to complete the wheel extension with the auxiliary pump before using the emergency CO_2 bottle which had been installed in all the latest models of this aircraft. My reluctance was out of consideration for the ground crews. These hardworking people would have to bleed all the hydraulic lines in the plane once they were filled with the CO_2 before repairing the leak and refilling with hydraulic fluid, a meticulous process consuming time as well as knuckle skin.

I pulled out the auxiliary pump handle from its position under the left side of the seat and pumped steadily while watching the needle on the gauge.

Nothing. It didn't budge.

I recalled a similar experience earlier in my training. That Corsair was an older model without the emergency CO_2 bottle, but I had successfully lowered the stuck gear by moving the control stick violently back and forth with the airplane slowed to about 85 knots. Although the Engineering Handbook had said quite clearly this would not work, it did. After three or four such episodes of violent contortions in the air (I had told the tower personnel of my intentions so they wouldn't think the aircraft had suddenly acquired an acute case of St. Vitus' dance) the gear, indeed, finally locked into place.

I tried the same procedure. Once again, the gear indicator refused to budge.

Reluctantly, I told the tower I was using the CO_2. Reaching back to the left side of the cockpit, I turned a small red knob. Sssst! Bloop! The wheels were all down and locked. I advised the tower and was cleared once again to land. Gingerly, I bounced one wheel, then the other, and they held. The rollout was completed, and I parked alongside some other Corsairs that had arrived the day before.

Almost immediately, a young Navy mechanic wheeled up in one of the little three-wheeled motorized towing devices designed for moving aircraft about the ramp but more often used to transport human cargo.

I could see he was, to put it mildly, upset.

"Lieutenant," he asked, "why'd you blow them wheels down with the CO_2?"

His question startled me as I had assumed the CO_2 device was designed and installed for just such occasions.

"Well," I replied, "landing with one main gear has a tendency to tear up the airplane, so I thought I'd use two."

"Yessir, I know," he rejoined. "But now we gotta bleed all them lines here in our line shop. If you had just bent the airplane, it would go over to O&R (overhaul and repair) and we wouldn't have to fool with it!"

No mention was made of the time I personally would probably have spent in "O&R" had I "just bent the airplane!"

Thus I learned that in the minds of some people I, too, was expendable.

Alone to San Diego

All pilots critique the techniques of all other pilots, even when the judges are mere passengers on the airplane. As a regular airline passenger while returning from my ferry flights, I developed a feeling of admiration and respect for the maneuvers of superbly skilled United Airlines pilots as they executed approaches and landings at Columbus in the teeth of an Ohio blizzard. After one missed approach because of the poor visibility and low ceiling, on the second pass we watched runway lights appear out of the blinding white vortex and the pilot went on to an on-schedule landing. At three o'clock in the morning, when the DC-3's wheels kissed the icy runway smoothly, the passenger next to me jerked awake.

"Uhmmm," he mumbled. "Here already?"

Such blissful unawareness of the years of training and thousands of hours of experience that make such flights possible was a tribute to the aviation profession. For me, it was interesting to note, that the airliner remained on the ground and the passengers destined for New York were taken to hotels for the night. A pilot must learn to refuse a flight that he feels may wind up with an unsanitary ending. That, in itself, is a valuable lesson.

The blizzard did not abate for several days, during which intermittent periods of comparative calm were punctuated with explosions of new wind and snow, making ferry flight under visual flight rules impossible.

Finally, after two weeks of idleness, relieved only by continuous games of "ferry pilot pool" in the ready room, the weather let up and delivery of aircraft resumed.

Pool was – in its various forms – almost the standard recreation in military ready rooms across the country, along with the continuing card games — bridge, poker, pinochle, and blackjack — and could be played while wearing a parachute harness (the chute itself, of course, remained in the airplane), so that when the next teletype sequence showed the weather to his next stop was flyable, the pilot was ready to leave immediately.

Some pilots' skill at these two pastimes garnered them more income than their service pay, usually based on an invitation such as:

"One game for half a clam while you're waiting, Lieutenant?" I learned quickly that accepting such an invitation offered only a remote possibility of my coming out ahead. But, with practice, my skill gradually improved, so that my cache of travel money was not seriously depleted.

* * *

Finally my name appeared on the Operations Board to fly Corsair 81721 to NZY (San Diego). Since I was scheduled to leave as early as possible in the morning, I spent an hour or so with my maps and the weather personnel. I recomputed the estimated time enroute between scheduled stops and tried to recall prominent landmarks along the route.

The anticipation and excitement of again flying the trip by myself were considerably tempered by the knowledge that my actual experience in this operation was still quite limited.

Since this was only my second transcontinental solo, there were a few butterflies in my midsection as I walked out to the Corsair and pulled the prop through to clear the oil out of the bottom cylinders. The lineman and I finished the preflight inspection, then I mounted the wing and settled into the cockpit. The comfortable feel of familiar surroundings soon dispelled any serious misgivings about the upcoming journey as I taxied out for takeoff.

The snowplow crews who had just finished clearing the runway waved as I rolled by. High snowbanks, the remnants of the blizzard, lined my takeoff roll when I hauled the airplane at a steep angle into the winter sky and headed west at 9 a.m.

Once the ship was cleaned up, trimmed, and on course at cruising altitude, there was very little for me to do. I monitored the checkpoints closely, performed the minor mental gymnastics necessary to compute my ground speed between them, and discovered that the usual prevailing westerly wind was there, but moderate. The new Corsair was moving across the Midwestern landscape at just under three miles a minute with the power settings at slow cruise. In addition, this time the windshield was free of any oil film.

Two and a quarter hours later, I reduced power for the descent into Lambert Field at St. Louis. The area between the runway and taxi strips indicated that the recent blizzard had passed this way also. It did seem to be a bit warmer as I pulled up to the parking area, pulled the mixture to idle cutoff, and hoisted my frame out of the cockpit.

A lineman walked up to me. "How's the weather in Columbus, Lieutenant?" he asked.

"Let's just not even discuss it," I replied, with a grimace.

"It's been pretty cold here, too," he said. "Got down to 18 degrees the other morning." He shivered as he recalled that frosty day.

Line personnel at various bases were particularly aware of the vagaries of the weather. They were obliged to endure all manner of howling winds, driving snow, or blistering heat, while seeing that the aircraft charged to them were properly chocked, tied down, replenished with fuel and oil — even if the oil barely flowed from the spout because of the cold — and prepared for flight on schedule. Each had our respect and admiration.

After four and a half hours of flying time, the lunch stop at Tulsa was routine, complete with peanut butter and jelly sandwiches, carrots, and milk — the Navy long since had learned the efficacy of carrots in keeping our eyes in good shape.

Ft. Worth appeared ahead about four in the afternoon, local time, so I decided to RON. As I rolled up to the Navy's parking facility and cut the engine, a 5,000-gallon high-octane fuel truck pulled up in front of the Corsair. I was still sitting in the cockpit working on the logbook when its driver, a Navy chief petty officer, stepped into view, a large black cigar clenched in his teeth.

As he rounded the propeller tips, dragging the gasoline hose along, I saw cigar smoke encircling his head; with horror, I realized that the stogie was actually lit!

In utter disbelief, I watched as he mounted the fighter and proceeded to take the usual fueling position astraddle the round fuselage ahead of the cockpit. He opened the small access hatch and reached for the fuel cap, setting the stage to add some 75 gallons of 100-octane aviation gasoline to the main fuel tank.

Before he could open the fuel cap, releasing the aromatic and highly flammable gasoline fumes, I stood up in the cockpit and, for the first time in my military career, read off an enlisted man.

"Mister," I exploded, "you will put out that cigar right now and if you ever try to gas my airplane again with one in your mouth, I'll bust you down to seaman second so fast you won't even have time to pack your flat hat. Do you read me, Mister?"

He read me all right. A look of startled bewilderment flooded his face as he climbed down and snubbed the cigar on the truck tire. He then threw it into the trash bin on the side of the vehicle.

"I'm sorry, sir," he said, contritely. "I plumb forgot about havin' it."

I believed him. The association of fire and its destructive characteristics with his smoking is nearly always forgotten by the smoker. The intake of nicotine in the smoke, I suppose, becomes so much a part of the smoker's formula of life that he unconsciously loses his cognizance of the real danger of the smoke and fire in his cigar, pipe, or cigarette. He was totally oblivious not only to the danger to his own body systems but to his surrounding environment which, at the moment, included me, a $75,000 airplane, and a big fuel truck full of 100-octane avgas.

"Oh, so you forgot it!" I steamed. "Do you have the foggiest idea what would happen to you, me, and this row of combat airplanes if that truckload ignited? You better shape up, Chief, or go back to pushing 'boots.' "

He seemed properly chastised as I started over to the Operations Office with my small zipper bag that I had retrieved from under the cockpit seat. Another lineman fell in alongside of me, matching my steps.

"Thanks, Lieutenant," he said. "We've been tellin' the chief about his cigars a long time, but that's the first time he ever got really chewed out about 'em. I think he's got the word now."

"Let's hope so," I gritted, and went on into the office, still steaming.

I filled out the day's report and signed the RON list. This latter form was always completed at the end of each day's ferry flight arrivals at each station along the various routes. The home squadron of each pilot was then advised by teletype as to his location. In this way, should any mishap occur enroute and a pilot not show on the list, an immediate search and rescue operation could be initiated to locate him. Therefore, failure to check in on the RON list could have embarrassing consequences. The resulting expense of both a "false search" and its attendant paperwork could make the errant pilot wish the search had really been necessary.

My first day on the airways on my second trip alone had ended and all was well. The new airplane had performed perfectly, and the anticipation of the morrow's trek to San Diego included a feeling of euphoria. After a full day of flying, I was physically and mentally tired, so sleep came easily. But I couldn't imagine ever becoming weary of this job; the travel bug had bitten me.

* * *

The next morning's trip across Texas included a 10 a.m. stop in Midland at the Army Air Corps base there. The military activity had transformed the normally quiet cattle and oil community into a boom town. The slow drawls of Texas were now punctuated with the clipped accents of Chicago and the broad A's of New England. This commingling of our nation's various cultures was not without some trauma, most of which originated in the various bars when the thin veneer of civility was eroded by the consumption of various libations sold in those establishments. The resulting bruises, contusions, broken noses, and chipped teeth kept both civilian and military physicians and dentists consistently occupied.

One delightful characteristic of the air base at Midland, however, made it a favorite overnight stop for all informed ferry pilots. Even though it was a $3.00 stop, the fare at the Mess Hall was outstanding. It seems that, even in the midst of wartime meat rationing, the enterprising personnel in the supply section had arranged a suitable liaison with some of the local cattle growers whereby they obtained whole sides of beef for the base's larder. Such carcasses were carefully aged in the refrigerated confines of Mess Hall storage facilities and were then cut into the most delicious steaks west of the Waldorf. Such gastronomic delights cost the monumental sum of $1.25 − with all the trimmings. So, even as a $3.00 stop, Midland's popularity was assured.

After breakfast the next morning, I saddled up again, westward. El Paso was bypassed; the next stop was Coolidge, Arizona, for fuel.

The leg took a little over three hours, but I had picked up an hour by going through another time zone. I filed for San Diego, arriving at about 4 p.m., Pacific Time.

Parking my second solo delivery at the receiving ramp, I lifted my parachute out of the cockpit, reached under the seat for my little bag, and climbed down.

My briefcase, with my carefully marked maps inside, was left alongside the right edge of the seat.

After signing off the airplane at the Delivery Office, I boarded the shuttle bus (named the cattle wagon because of its open sides and enormous capacity) and rode over to the Naval Air Transport System (NATS) terminal to arrange passage back to Columbus.

The daily R4D flight left at 6 p.m., so I had time for a bite to eat, to check my two pieces of luggage, and get aboard for the trip to home base.

The NATS airline was extraordinarily efficient, and was run very much like a commercial air carrier. The pilots were mostly former airline pilots pressed into service with the necessary rank to allow a pay scale commensurate with their civilian earnings. Even the aircraft they flew were the same popular and ubiquitous DC-3 Douglas transports dubbed R4D by the Navy. Copilots were usually Naval Aviators who had completed operational training in transport aircraft and were assigned to NATS to build time for overseas logistics support duty.

We departed San Diego on time and headed for our first stop in Amarillo, Texas. As the wheels of the R4D receded into their retracted position in the engine nacelles, I suddenly remembered. My maps! They were still in the Corsair!

After mentally kicking myself, I calmed down. They were, after all, expendable items and I could always get some more. But the

Navy clerk would surely demand an explanation of how I could "expend" them so fast. Also, the leather briefcase in which the maps were carried had cost me $12.87 in downtown Columbus. Certainly they would be found before the fighter was shipped to the Fleet, and I could retrieve them on my next trip.

Cabin heaters on the pre-war DC-3 airliner left a lot to be desired. Hot air ducts were arranged so that while one's upper body was fairly comfortable, one's feet slowly turned to blocks of ice. Such was the case on our five-and-a-half-hour winter night flight to Amarillo.

The weather was most cooperative for the first half of the segment. But, just a bit past Phoenix, it began to deteriorate. First, there was a slight trembling of the airplane's fuselage as we began to enter the cumulus clouds. Then the moments of perfect smoothness followed by the "whump-caroom!" of the violent up and down drafts of a cumulo-nimbus thunderhead. The seatbelt sign was on, of course, but few aboard saw it since they were dozing. I had anticipated the buffeting and had cinched my belt tight. Fortunately no one hit the ceiling, but all belts were promptly fastened and remained so through the instrument approach to the Army Air Base at Amarillo.

There we learned firsthand about the completely aberrant weather of the Texas Panhandle and the true meaning of the expression "weathered in." Rain, ice, snow, high gusty winds, blowing dust and sand — West Texas has it all!

We were assigned quarters in the transient barracks area until the weather again became flyable. Four days and two unlaundered shirts later, we reassembled in the NATS area of the sprawling Amarillo Air Base, which was covered with a foot of fresh snow, and boarded our venerable R4D. Mercifully, it had been hangared, so it was not necessary to rid it of ice and snow. The weather was still overcast and gusty, but had returned to a status where, at least, flight operation under Instrument Flight Rules (IFR) were possible and the runways had been plowed.

Our next stop after we left the wind-swept environs of the northwest corner of Texas was the Olathe, Kansas, Naval Air Station, where I had begun my flight training as a Naval Aviation Cadet only a year and a half before.

The weather at Olathe was still marginal but, after an instrument-approach landing and while the big R4D was refueling, we had lunch, then departed for Columbus, about four hours away.

I had discovered that the pilot of this leg of the NATS trip was a former civilian flying classmate, Sid Herndon, from my days in Chattanooga. I was standing in the passageway behind the pilot's seat visiting with him, each of us filling the other in on our experiences since our days in the Waco.

The layers of cloud through which we were flying had occasional spots of perfectly clear visibility. But, since there was no horizon or other reference point, Herndon flew strictly by reference to flight instruments on the panel, and he was good at it.

We were between Springfield, Illinois, and St. Louis on an easterly course about two hours from Columbus when, during one of the clear intervals, both of us picked up in our left peripheral vision arc an object crossing left to right 90 degrees to our course and only 100 feet below us. It was another DC-3 airliner.

Our glances followed it during the four or five seconds it took to pass underneath. Herndon checked his altimeter, which read precisely 7,000 feet, our altitude assigned by air traffic control.

"I guess he's descending into St. Louis," Herndon said, finally, with a shrug.

"It would be nice if there were some way the controllers could tell us about guys like that," I said, dimly aware that just such a

101

device was already in use in combat areas. Called radar, the acronym for Radio Detection And Ranging, it was so hush-hush that no one ever discussed it in public. By bouncing a radio signal off an airplane and measuring its time to return, both distance and bearing from the station could be determined with great accuracy. True, the system was still in its infancy, but it would only be a matter of time, I was sure, until it would make our task of avoiding one another in the sky much easier.

We droned along in silence for a while until Herndon, turning to his copilot, said, "Get Indianapolis on the horn and see what the weather's like in Columbus."

His copilot tuned in the station and asked for an update on our destination weather. Partial clearing was expected at our arrival time, so in a few minutes Herndon asked to start his letdown into the murky sky over the Dayton-Columbus area. I noticed he specifically asked if the controller had any reported traffic in the area.

"Negative," he replied. "I guess you're it this afternoon." The controller proceeded to give Herndon clearance into Columbus.

The wheels made their usual "runch-runch" sound as Herndon landed on the runway threshold numbers and gently allowed the tail to drop. I had taken my seat for the landing. As we pulled onto the ramp and stopped, I unbuckled my seatbelt, gathered my luggage and parachute bag, and waited for Herndon and his copilot.

"You always land like that, Lucky?" I asked, throwing the usual question at him. "I don't think I'll even need a chiropractor."

Herndon grinned. "Not quite like a Waco," he replied.

We shook hands, and he went across the ramp to file for the last leg of his trip, which terminated in New York. It had been a pleasant and nostalgic reminder of the days of CPTP. Herndon had almost quit the program when he entered the aerobatic phase, but "stuck it out" and made the grade. He was an excellent pilot.

I checked in at the Squadron Office in the gathering dusk to complete my second delivery as a lead pilot.

Only the night duty officer was left, along with the yeoman, in the office. It turned out to be Hank Barker, one of my former squadron mates during Operational Training in Corsairs. Although he had not been in my particular flight group, we had become well acquainted and enjoyed one another's company.

"Well," he said. "I see you found your way once again to the West Coast and back. Any problems?"

"Not until we were weathered in at Amarillo coming back on NATS. Here's hoping my laundry's back. And what time does the Disbursing Office open in the morning?"

He laughed as I revealed my affliction with a common ferry pilot problem: an acute shortage of shirts, shorts, socks, and money.

"0800," he said, "and I think you've got a few bucks in the till. By the way, your name's going to be on the board tomorrow for another flight."

"Well, you know how it is with us old-timers in this business. We're in demand, and duty calls."

I said good night and headed for the Officers' Mess to relieve the emptiness in my midsection. As I headed for the barracks and bed, I wondered what my next delivery and destination would be.

My musings made effective lullabies as I didn't really care about the details, just as long as I was flying some place. Ferry flying was obviously addictive, and I was hooked.

Curtiss Novelty

My name was indeed on the flight assignment board at the Operations Office the next morning. Having replenished my hip pocket at the Disbursing Office and my clothes at the base laundry, I was all ready for another trip.

I was posted to deliver a Curtiss SC-1 Seahawk to Norfolk. There was also a note ordering me to report forthwith to the Operations Officer.

When I presented myself at his office, he came right to the point, "Ever fly an SC-1 Seahawk?"

"No, sir. What's an SC-1 Seahawk?"

I had heard rumors of a new carrier scout plane being readied for the Fleet in the Curtiss factory across the field from our squadron area, but had never seen one.

"Well," the officer explained, "it's actually a seaplane, but the factory installs wheel gear for ferrying it across country. Supposed to be quite an airplane. The guys in the hangar have nicknamed it the 'Curtiss Duckhawk.' Here's the handbook on it. Read it, then go get yourself checked out in it. They want it down at Norfolk tomorrow for evaluation."

Just like that. "Get yourself checked out and take it to Norfolk tomorrow." They certainly didn't fool around with much formal training here. He did give me the Engineering Handbook on the airplane, so I anticipated no trouble. After all, I'd flown strange airplanes before and all aircraft have the same basic characteristics.

I hurried directly over to the hangar to see what the people at Curtiss had dreamed up for scout duty in the Pacific.

The Curtiss scout was parked all by itself in the front corner of the hangar. A bit smaller than the Corsair, with a stubby round fuselage and fairly short squared-off wings, its single-seat cockpit had what pilots call a "birdcage" sliding canopy (so named because of the latticework frames holding the plexiglass bubble shape of the streamlined enclosure). The canopy structure stuck up from the fuselage as if it had been almost overlooked. Then I remembered this was after all a scout plane, and such an arrangement provided the pilot excellent visibility in all directions.

The engine was the time-proven Wright 1,050-horsepower radial coupled to a four-bladed electric propeller, which would be a new experience for me.

The propeller pitch was controlled by an electric motor in the hub rather than by a hydraulic cylinder actuated by the engine oil as in the Corsair. I had heard all sorts of unkind rumors about the malfunctions of electric props so was not entirely enthusiastic about this assignment. The efficiency of the propeller governor device that changes and holds the pitch of the blades of the propeller can be very critical.

My concern with the electric propeller was due to its alleged proclivity for going into completely flat pitch at critical times of flight (such as takeoff), thereby instantly replacing top rated thrust with total drag and also allowing the engine, without air resistance on the propeller, to "run away" and disintegrate like a bomb. However, I knew that this airplane was equipped with the latest design of such propellers, so was almost satisfied that it was up to the job at hand.

The landing gear was the most incongruous looking part of the plane. It had, in fact, been added as an afterthought, replacing the single main float on the bottom of the fuselage, the normal seaplane configuration. Also, the usual wing tip floats had been removed for ferrying purposes. Two stubby landing gear struts sticking out of the fuselage just behind the engine nacelle supported the narrow-span landing wheels. The illusion was of a duck out of water. No wonder it was dubbed "Duckhawk."

While sitting in the cockpit, I scanned through the handbook, familiarizing my hands and eyes with the locations and movements of various controls and gauges. After several simulated blindfold checks, in which I closed my eyes and put my hands on individual switches and levers, I believed I was ready to fly the Seahawk, locally – at first.

The ungainly critter was towed out of the hangar and the lineman pulled the propeller through several times to distribute the oil properly to all cylinders. I took a deep breath, pulled my parachute straps tighter, and signalled that I was ready to go.

Starting this engine involved a cartridge starter like those used on the early model Corsairs back in Green Cove Springs, Florida. Such starters used a small cylinder and piston arrangement, with the power supplied by the gases from an exploding cartridge, like an oversized shotgun shell, to spin the prop.

The shell was placed into a breech positioned in the side of the cockpit. The device was closed and locked in place. After the engine cylinders were primed with fuel, the cartridge was electrically fired by pushing a starter button in the cockpit. The cylinder and piston system was geared to the crankshaft of the engine like a conventional starter, and the resulting surge of power turned the engine over. If the fuel/air mixture was just right, if the spark plugs were not fouled, if it was not too cold outside, and if one uttered a word of prayer, the engine would usually start.

Since the cockpit cartridge supply holder held only eight rounds, all pilots hoped that starting would not be a long, drawn-out process; after two or three cartridges were fired, a lengthy cooling-off period was necessary or the whole system could be damaged by excessive heat and pressure. The sole advantage of such a starting system was that no heavy battery and starter motor were required. The resulting saving in weight could be used for additional fuel, making the scout plane more effective for its designed purpose.

After one unsuccessful attempt, the engine started with the second cartridge and, when the oil pressure came up, I advanced the throttle and tentatively taxied out to the end of the runway. Clumsy-looking or not, the SC-1 seemed to handle easily enough on the ground and forward visibility was much better than in the Corsair.

I set the brakes and ran up the engine to check the magnetos. As the rpm's passed 1,900, a curious thing happened: The tail started to rise.

I immediately cut the power back to idle and the tail descended, before the propeller blades dug into the asphalt, with the resultant reduction in propeller blade length after which the entire prop hub blade assembly would have to be torn down and inspected. As for me, a likely court-martial would have ensued wherein I would have had to explain why I didn't know of this characteristic if I had read an obscure line in the handbook, an asterisked item at the bottom of the page:

"Do not exceed 1,900 R.P.M. during ground runup of the engine in this aircraft. Sufficient elevator control is not available with wheel gear installed to prevent nose-over."

With both magnetos checked out and the electric prop properly cycled, I called the tower, received a takeoff clearance, and slowly pushed the throttle forward. Acceleration was rapid and the Seahawk came off at about 65 mph.

Pulling the power back to rated climb manifold pressure and adjusting the electric propeller to 2,600 rpm, I noticed that the rate-of-climb instrument showed we were climbing like the proverbial homesick angel, about 1,800 feet per minute. This ugly duckling was quite an airplane.

Upon reaching 10,000 feet, I leveled off and proceeded to check the maneuverability of my new mount. Although it was obviously not designed to be as nimble as a fighter, it did a passable slow roll − though a bit heavy on the ailerons − and looped okay. Now to check the slow flight performance, the only way for a pilot to learn when and how an airplane approached a stall − and how it stalls. This is necessary to be able to make landings at the proper airspeed.

Carefully, I edged the throttle back, watching the air speed back off toward stall. As the first slight shudder of the approaching stall was felt, it was so mild that instead of adding power and dropping the nose, I pulled the stick all the way back and kicked full left rudder; not to worry − this was a baby carriage.

The spin was immediate.

The "baby carriage" really unwound: one turn, two, three −

To recover, I popped the stick forward and fed in full right rudder.

The spin stopped promptly with the airplane in a slight dive, so I eased the stick back until we were again in level flight. I glanced at the altimeter − it read 7,000 feet! We had lost 3,000 feet in perhaps 15 seconds!

In a spin, this airplane really dropped like a greased anvil! Also, I had noticed as I stopped the spin that the nose was beginning to come up with no effort on my part, which gave me pause. I'd have to check that flight characteristic out in the handbook when I finished reading it later in the afternoon.

Having spent a little over an hour practicing stalls in the familiarization process, I spiraled down, entered the traffic pattern at Columbus, and landed.

Putting the SC-1 back on terra firma was a piece of cake since it landed more slowly than the Corsair. With the wheel gear installed, the center of gravity was far to the rear so there was no tendency to porpoise. It remained firmly planted on the runway as I spilled the flaps and rolled into a parking place.

"How'd it go, sir?" the lineman asked, climbing on the wing to help me unplug from the cockpit.

"No sweat," I replied, insouciantly. "Not a bad airplane."

There was no need to mention my misgivings about the strange spin characteristics until I got another look at the handbook.

He assured me the Seahawk would be gassed and ready to go to Norfolk first thing the next morning.

* * *

After lunch, I found a seat in the ready room and continued my perusal of the SC-1 Manual. As I reached the section entitled "Restrictions," I read the usual ones regarding taxiing too fast, failure to remove the spent cartridge in the starter before it cools (it "swells and sticks in place if not removed promptly"), excessive brake use (it "wears out the disks"), plus all the other "boilerplate" the people who write the manuals put in them to earn their pay.

Then I noticed an asterisk in the "Restricted Flight Maneuvers" section:

"Under no circumstances is this aircraft to be placed in a spin with wheel gear installed. Because of the rearward location of the center of gravity when the flotation gear is absent, the aircraft develops a 'flat spin' from which recovery is virtually impossible. This occurs after the third or fourth turn of the spin."

The words swam before my eyes; I had been just plain lucky. One more turn and I would have had to leave the uncontrollable airplane by taking my first lesson in parachute jumping. The airplane would, of course, have been a total loss, a court martial offense, for sure. I firmly resolved to read future handbooks completely before checking out in any more single-seat airplanes. Next time my guardian angel might not be holding my hand.

The morning dawned clear and cold. However, since the Seahawk had been in the hangar, the oil would be warm, so the engine started on the first cartridge, an auspicious beginning.

Promptly at 9:30 a.m., we lifted off and headed for Norfolk, slightly more than 400 miles southeast.

My course took me about 20 miles south of Zanesville, Ohio. I crossed the Ohio River into West Virginia just north of Marietta at 7,500 feet. The outside air thermometer was showing exactly 15 degrees, but the cockpit heater and the hazy sunshine kept it reasonably comfortable inside.

About 20 miles west of Elkins, West Virginia, while I was looking down at the tortuous territory, my composure was rudely interrupted by a loud "Whap!"

My scalp prickled. I was not experiencing illusory "automatic rough;" something on the airplane had really come loose. The initial sound was following by a continuing flapping noise: "Whappity, whappity, whap, whap!" from the rear section of the plane.

Reflexively, I cinched up my parachute straps preparatory to departing the airplane, even though the terrain below was absolute wilderness; I was sure the tail surfaces were either already gone or would be leaving shortly. However, the stick was steady in my hand and the airplane's flight attitude and operation were completely normal, except for that alarming ominous fluttering noise aft.

Gingerly, I moved the stick and rudder around a bit. The airplane responded promptly and smoothly. No problems with control. I did notice a draft in the cockpit enclosure, however, and an increase in the noise level.

The chart showed a civilian airport next to a river just south of Elkins. Throttling back, I headed for it, circled the field to check the windsock, and landed. Taxiing up to the parking ramp, I noticed that the Seahawk was the object of everyone's attention on the airport. I pulled the mixture control back and the engine whined to a stop. I exited the cockpit, jumped down on the wing, and immediately saw the source of all the racket.

Apparently, after the cockpit canopy was designed in its streamlined, bubble-shaped configuration and production had started, some test pilot had discovered that air pressures created by the slipstream made it impossible to open the canopy while the airplane was in flight.

Since Navy regulations decreed that all aircraft canopies be open on landing − and of course it is also necessary to slide the canopy back if the pilot must bail out − a quick-fix solution to the problem was evolved that would not deter production of the model for the Fleet.

Since the pilot could not twist his head far enough to see through the extreme back panels anyway, the canopy's two rearmost plexiglass panels were simply chopped open and new ones were installed, held in place by two snap fasteners affixed to the fabric binding of the two sections of plexiglass.

But, as I had just discovered, prolonged flight at cruising speed gradually loosened the snap fasteners and they let go, allowing the panels to flap in the breeze with the resulting ungodly racket that was so unsettling to a pilot's nerves.

Having ascertained the cause, I simply completed unfastening both offending panels and stowed them in the cockpit, then walked nonchalantly over to the airport lunchroom and had a sandwich and glass of milk while answering the questions of the local gentry about this "strange-looking Navy plane."

After this brief noon repast, I strolled in my most professional military pilot manner to where the SC-1 was parked, aware that every civilian eyeball on the field carefully cataloged each movement as I preflighted the Navy's airplane. Mounting the wing with all the athletic prowess I could muster, I resettled myself in the cockpit, withdrew a starting cartridge from the container in the side, and opened the starter breech to insert it into the chamber. There, staring me coldly in the eye, was the spent cartridge from the start I had made back at Columbus, now cold and firmly — perhaps permanently — stuck. No matter how many fingernails I broke, it wouldn't budge.

Completely chagrined, I asked one of the local mechanics for a screwdriver and a pair of pliers, while my "gallery" slowly dispersed. In a few minutes, he and I managed to dislodge the recalcitrant cartridge and insert the live one. I gave him the remains of the spent cartridge for a souvenir of the occasion, which seemed to be adequate compensation for his labors.

Since the engine was still warm, I primed it very little and cracked the throttle just a bit. The engine caught on the first cartridge and ran smoothly. I removed the still-smoking cartridge promptly this time, and tossed it to the mechanic. He grinned and gave me an okay sign with thumb and forefinger.

After takeoff, I felt it appropriate to make the occasion a memorable one for the folks at Elkins, so I banked around and came across the field at full bore in the expected salute to the hospitable people who had welcomed me when I dropped in uninvited. At the end of my pass, I lifted the nose into about a 30-degree climb, did a slow roll to the left and continued the climb up to cruising altitude.

During the climb I glanced toward the fuel gauge, which to my shock was showing a little less than half full. The Seahawk, which had a fantastically long range when equipped for its normal duty as a scout plane, carried most of its fuel in the main fuselage pontoon. It had only a three-hour fuel range when rigged with wheel gear for overland operations, which put Norfolk just about at the end of this limit when I left Columbus. Now the comparatively small amount of fuel carried in the ferry configuration, coupled with the brief interruption of the let-down and climb-out at Elkins, had consumed considerably more fuel than that used in normal cruising flight and Norfolk was out of range. However, after my hot-shot-pilot performance there, I simply couldn't go back.

Yet I didn't relish the idea of a quivering fuel gauge while I was entering traffic at the busy Naval Air Station. I decided to land for fuel at the Army Air Base at Richmond, Virginia, as it was almost 90 miles closer than Norfolk.

When the airfield at Richmond appeared, I called the tower.

"Richmond Army Tower, this is Navy 357, 10 northwest for landing your station."

"Roger, 357," the tower said. "Say type aircraft."

"Type aircraft SC-1 Seahawk," I replied.

Then, after a brief pause, I heard, "Ah, roger, 357. We don't have any water here."

"No problem," I said, and laughed. "I've got wheels on this one. They don't put the floats on until I get it to Norfolk. I need some 100-octane fuel."

I checked the gauge again. Yes, I needed fuel.

"Roger, 357," the tower said. "Give us a call downwind."

As I taxied up the parking ramp, I could see the tower personnel giving this strange-looking seaplane with wheels the once-over with their binoculars. Others followed the fuel truck over and checked out the Navy stranger.

I climbed down and showed the lineman the fueling procedure. I had used a little over two-thirds of my fuel thus far and probably would have made it to Norfolk but would have had no reserve for traffic delays, so my unprogrammed stop was completely justifiable. Just then I realized I would indeed be called upon to "justify" the stop — the little matter of the payment for the fuel.

"Who do we charge this to, Lieutenant?" the truck driver asked.

"Good question, Corporal," I said, confidently, although my mind was racing as to just which entity in our joint military effort would write the check for the Army fuel to be expended in a Navy aircraft. This decision could ultimately wind up at the highest levels, maybe even Congress.

I came up with a solution. Mustering all the authority my one gold bar could exude, I told him, "The usual procedure in these cases is for me to sign your fuel invoice." I was lying through my teeth, but he didn't know it. "Then your Finance Officer simply forwards it to my home ferry squadron in Columbus. I'll write the address on the form for you."

Taking the clipboard from him as nonchalantly as possible, I proceeded to write fictitious billing instructions on the invoice and signed it with an appropriate flourish.

"That should do it, Corporal," I said. "And I want to thank you and your crew for your assistance."

"No sweat, Lieutenant," he said. "Drop in any time."

So far so good. I climbed aboard and inserted another cartridge into the starter. Going quickly through my starting checklist, I lit off the radial engine and it caught as the third blade passed the top of the cowling. Again, I was careful to remove the used cartridge.

The tower cleared me to the runway and, after a quick check of the magnetos before takeoff, I shoved the throttle and departed the premises. In my haste, I had forgotten to roll the trim tab forward after landing so the zoom takeoff and steep climb out of Richmond were, to say the least, spectacular to the ground observers, even though I held the stick forward while feverishly rolling the tab to its proper takeoff position. Before I reached the airport boundary, the altimeter showed 1,000 feet.

The tower controllers had noticed. "Some problem, 357?" the voice asked?.

"Negative," I responded, trying to sound as unconcerned as possible. "Guess I'm just not accustomed to the climb rate on this new machine yet."

The tower man pretended he had bought my explanation.

"Roger, 357," he said, in the flat intonation typical of controllers. "See you later." In the background was the sound of laughter.

About ten minutes out, well along the way to Norfolk, the anticipated call came through the earphones.

"Navy 357! Navy 357! This is Richmond tower. You still on frequency?"

Concluding that under the circumstances silence was the best policy at that point, I did not respond. Richmond tower repeated the call twice, then gave up. I probably would have to explain the $62 fuel bill to the Finance Officer in Columbus and fill out several forms, but for now, the Army's 100-octane was purring merrily away in the Navy's engine four feet in front of me, and I was almost to Norfolk.

The Naval Air Station at Norfolk is about seven miles east of the city in a tidelands area just west of the ocean. As I entered traffic to land, I couldn't help thinking that about 50 miles south on Kill Devil Hill at Kitty Hawk, the Wright brothers first achieved powered, controllable, man-carrying flight. Looking around the machine that was supporting me in the air in comfort at the dizzy speed of 150 miles an hour and at the maze of instruments that allowed us to fly when we couldn't even see outside, aviation advances since the Wright brothers' first aeroplane were hard to comprehend.

The nostalgic reverie was cut short by the necessity of running through the landing checklist while maintaining vigilance for other traffic. I grinned at the thought that the Wright brothers were the last pilots who didn't have to be concerned about the possibility of a midair collision with another airplane. The tower personnel at Norfolk were quite skillful at fitting me into traffic, however, and soon I was on the taxi strip.

"Where do you suppose I'm to deliver this little jewel?" I asked the tower's ground control.

"Just taxi over to the west ramp and somebody'll meet you."

I did as he said, and was directed by a gesticulating lineman to a spot in front of a large hangar marked "Test-Receiving."

As the propeller made its last revolution of the day, the line crew, the mechanics, and even some clerical personnel came over to look at their new toy.

One of my colleagues in a flight suit with the Navy's gold wings and a lieutenant (j.g.)'s silver bar on his collar strolled over, stuck out his hand, and said, "I'm Pete Watson. How's it handle?"

"No problems that amount to anything," I said. "Just a little feisty with the wheel gear and no center float attached."

I told him about the experience with the canopy flapping at Elkins and showed him the guilty panels.

"Yeah," Watson said. "We heard there were some problems with the canopy. Does it open okay now?"

"Smooth as glass, but a little chilly and noisy inside. Guess I'll go thaw out my hands and write the whole deal up on the yellow sheet."

Watson walked over with me and we discussed the characteristics of the Seahawk. His job was to check it out for the Fleet as soon as the float gear was installed, so he was skillfully picking my brains for all the useful information he could get. As always, the conversation with a fellow pilot was most enjoyable and I did my best to impart whatever information I had gleaned from my four hours' occupancy in the cockpit.

He showed me how to get to the NATS Office and we parted company.

I made arrangements for my return to Columbus. The flight didn't leave until 5 p.m., so I relaxed for a few minutes at the lunch counter in the passenger lounge of the Navy's airline and eased the hunger pangs. It was now considerably past noon, and I could use some body fuel.

The trip back to Columbus took only two and a half hours in the NATS R4D so it was only 7:30 p.m. when I reported back at my home squadron.

Barker was still Duty Officer as I entered with my parachute and green zipper bag.

"Quick trip, huh?" he asked. "How's the new Curtiss product do on cross country?"

I filled him in on the efficacy of the Curtiss factory personnel in the design of cockpit canopies and assured him that, aside from that one minor flaw, it was a well-designed airplane and should be a valuable addition to the Fleet's air arm.

I also told him about the spurious fiduciary arrangements I had made at the Army Air Base at Richmond for my fuel.

He grinned broadly. "You'll probably hear about that," he said, shaking his head.

Strangely, I never did.

The $62 is probably still showing as a "suspense item" on some government account in Washington, D.C.

A pair of aces

Personnel of all squadrons come from all walks of life and from all parts of the United States. Each squadron is, therefore, a microcosm of the entire country with all the different cultures, dialects, and temperaments. In any ready room, the clipped semi-British dialects of New England mix with the slow drawl of Texas, the flat twang of Kansas, and the rounded-off participles of the deep South. Some of the personalities found in such associations can be quite colorful.

Two such characters in our ferry group — both Marine lieutenants — became renowned for their insouciant activities that provided conversational fodder for ferry pilot ready rooms all over the country.

Tom Woodward, whose name had been abbreviated to "Woodie," and Timothy O'Toole, whose Irish ancestry probably contributed to his affinity for Irish whiskey and his readiness to participate in occasional breaches of what he considered unnecessary regulation, had flown together since basic flight training and were natural pilots. Although they were smart and intelligent, neither of these free spirits had ever permitted bookwork or regulations to interfere with his aeronautical education and/or activities.

To the fuming consternation of the Ferry Command, they frequently detoured on side trips when enroute together, straying off the prescribed ferry routes and their off-agenda caprices often contributed to the aviation and social histories of small hamlets all the way across the country. They began their ferrying careers by engaging in such diverting larks as flying fighter aircraft in formation at 250 mph down the main streets of small —and a few large — towns along the way, then pulling up into slow rolls away from one another, leaving the peace and quiet of the communities in total shambles.

121

Identification was impossible since the sudden arrival and departure speeds – as well as the face-down positions of the citizens – did not permit the recording of the large white numbers painted on the tails of the Corsairs. When the inevitable complaints were filed by irate city fathers with their Congressmen, they would be told that "Such maneuvers are necessary in carrying out the required missions in the war effort, and it is hoped the inconvenience is not too severe." The pilot duo at least had a policy not to dust-up the same town twice.

One April day, Woodie and O'Toole, with some of their squadron mates, were dispatched to Grosse Pointe, Michigan, in the squadron's R4D for a special ferry assignment.

Upon arrival, they learned that all pilots would check out in wartime versions of the Stinson 105, designated by the Navy as OY-1. The two-place, high-wing, fixed-gear light aircraft, powered by a 150-horsepower Franklin engine turning a fixed-pitch propeller, had greenhouse-type plexiglass windows all around to provide excellent visibility from the cockpit. The OY-1 was to be deployed for scouting and courier work in the South Pacific.

Slots in the leading edge of the outboard wing panels maintained a smooth flow of air across the wings at speeds at which other aircraft would have long since stalled and quit flying; with its huge flaps, an OY-1 was highly maneuverable at low airspeeds and could be landed in a very small space. Fighter pilots Woodie and O'Toole groused about having to check out in the little "toy airplanes" – as they called the OY-1's – and did it in short order when they were assigned to deliver two of them from Detroit to San Diego. At the leisurely 120-mph cruising airspeed of the OY-1, it was to take at least four days to reach the West Coast. This offered an opportunity that could be stretched into a series of social encounters by the brace of aces.

The first day they made not quite 450 miles, to St. Louis, before weather grounded them. After signing the required RON form, they proceeded to remain overnight, that night, the next night, and the night after that cutting a pair of wide swaths in the fields of friendly femininity.

Ideally for them, the weather remained sufficiently marginal that the local FCLO (Ferry Control Liaison Officer) couldn't offer them much of an argument when they would call in and report with straight faces that they had checked aviation weather and that it was not adequate for visual flight, as required by the regulations.

On the fourth morning, however, the weather was clear so they regretfully agreed it would be militarily prudent to continue their journey. An hour after takeoff, the cumulative effect of the previous three nights' visits to various eating and drinking establishments in St. Louis suddenly took its assertive toll on Woodie's digestive tract; the hapless pilot found it immediately necessary to descend and relieve the urgent call. Advising O'Toole by radio of his plight and intentions, Woodward selected a lush, green meadow and adroitly proceeded to use the short field capabilities of the OY-1. Not until the wheels sank into the surface did the smooth green field prove to be a crop of winter wheat about twelve inches high.

Somehow, Woodie managed to keep the OY-1 from nosing over on landing. He cut the switches, exited the aircraft and, while O'Toole circled lazily overhead like a huge hawk, speedily got on with the business for which the landing was made. Only then did he contemplate the serious issue of balancing the takeoff capabilities of the OY-1 against the entangling drag of foot-high wheat rippling in the breeze. After chewing his lip for a few moments, he decided he would try it. Jazzing the restarted engine, he turned into the wind, dropped 20 degrees of flaps, and pushed the throttle full forward. Slowly, the aircraft started to roll.

At about 30 miles per hour, long stems of wheat became thoroughly entwined in the wheels and flipped the struggling

aircraft on its back. Woodie, hanging inverted in the seatbelt, cut the switches and unsnapped the belt buckle to get out.

Gravity, of course, immediately took over, and Woodie's head struck part of the welded steel framework of the overhead portion of the inverted cockpit. Fortunately, it was a glancing blow and merely knocked him unconscious. As he lay in a helpless heap in the overturned airplane, slowly regaining his senses, he became aware of the apparition of a face flushed with anger at the cockpit window, and a wrathful voice snarling, "Who's gonna pay for my crop?"

The farmer claimed that a considerable area of his labors in the wheat field had just been nullified by Woodie's activities through the wheat during the landing and ill-fated takeoff attempt, and he demanded compensation. He had no concern about Woodie's aching head or possible other injuries, or for the $12,000 worth of government airplane that had just been reduced to junk.

Slowly Woodie extricated himself from his defunct aerial steed and waved to the circling O'Toole to signal to him that he was okay. O'Toole acknowledged by rocking his wings and continued on course to Springfield. Then he assured the farmer that all would be well if he could just use his telephone a few minutes.

This seemed to relieve the tension of the situation somewhat. The animosity of the wheat field proprietor slightly abated. He even inquired about Woodie's physical well-being.

"Pretty mean lump on your head there, son," he said. "You okay now?"

"I think so," Woodie replied, mentally castigating himself for so stupidly releasing his seatbelt while in an inverted position.

Almost invariably when an airplane winds up inverted on the ground as a result of some malfunction on the part of the pilot and/or the airplane, the natural instinct is to unfasten the seatbelt and get out. One simply forgets the fact that the belt is holding him in place. If this restraint is removed, a sore head at the very least or a broken neck at the worst can result. Accident reports document this phenomenon regularly, so Woodie was not alone in the record books.

A phone call to the FCLO in St. Louis set the wheels in motion to get the whole event squared away. The by-then friendly farmer insisted on driving Woodie into town to allow a physician to inspect the big bump on his head. The elderly practitioner pronounced him reasonably fit and issued the usual "Man wasn't meant to fly" admonition with the suggestion that Woodie take up some other line of work.

Woodie assured him he was considering it, which at the moment was probably true, although not by choice.

O'Toole landed at Springfield, Missouri, for fuel and confirmed Woodie's misfortune, but was told that he had to complete the delivery of his OY-1 on schedule. He filed for Tulsa and finished the trip straight and level with no side excursions.

Woodie, meanwhile, was invited to remain overnight at the farmer's house. The combination of good food, an excellent bed, and the privilege of explaining the mission of Marine Corps aviation to the farm couple's eighteen-year-old daughter made Woodie's day turn out far better than he had anticipated while on his back in the OY-1.

Regaling his young hostess with the fascinating history of his military career, suitably embellished for the occasion, consumed most of the evening. Although the thought of becoming better acquainted with the young lady crossed Woodie's mind, he had noticed the shotgun propped in a corner near the door and discretion dictated that he not incur any further claim for damage to the farmer's produce. He therefore retired to his room for some much-needed sleep, gathering strength to meet the Navy's salvage team arriving the next day.

The lieutenant (j.g.) in charge of the aircraft retrieval unit was unemotionally proficient at his job. Although thoroughly familiar with accident-generating idiosyncrasies of aircraft and their pilots, he was not a flyer himself, and his entire attitude toward Naval Aviators, Marine pilots in particular, was one of complete disdain. This is perhaps understandable since his continuing liaison with aircraft and pilots was invariably the result of some malfunction of either or both, and his job was to clean up the results.

"Why did you land in the unauthorized field, Woodward?" he asked, fingering his multi-page accident report form.

"The oil pressure was low, sir," Woodie said, feeling it would not be in his best interest to reveal the true reason for the stop in the wheat field.

"Couldn't you see the wheat was too high for the wheels of your aircraft?" the investigating officer asked, revealing his complete lack of any aviation knowledge. It is impossible to ascertain the depth of a crop such as wheat from 1,000 feet. From that height it looks like a perfectly smooth grassy field.

"No, sir," Woodie said, trying to explain. "You see, from altitude, it's impossible —"

"Oh, never mind," the lieutenant (j.g.) said, petulantly cutting Woodie off. "Tell it to the Operations Officer in Columbus," and issued Woodie a transportation request: an intercity bus back to St. Louis, then via airline to Columbus.

What with a chance acquaintance with a young lady on the bus and other unplanned delays, Woodie eventually arrived in Columbus four days later.

The Operations Officer lost no time in calling him on the carpet.

"Woodward, this report says you landed in the unauthorized location because of allegedly low oil pressure in the engine of the OY-1, " he began. "That engine probably only had ten hours on it, so just why would the oil pressure be low?"

"Sir," Woodie said, "I don't know. Perhaps it wasn't actually low. Maybe the gauge was off. They sometimes get pieces of grit in the line and they don't read right," he added, brightly.

Although Woodie's story was a complete fabrication, this was indeed a valid reason for a low oil pressure reading. Gauge errors do happen on new airplanes from time to time. A piece of aluminum from construction, or other debris, will find its way into the oil gauge line and cause a false reading. Woodie knew this and was using it as a ploy to avoid disciplinary action. A survival tactic, as it were.

"Woodward, what is the normal oil pressure for the engine in the OY-1?" the officer asked, studying the tent he had made with his fingers.

Woodie's composure suffered a severe setback at this question. He had no idea as to the correct oil pressure reading on the OY-1, or on any other airplane, for that matter. If the engine ran and no red lights showed on the panel, he would fly the airplane.

Why be concerned with where the needle pointed on some stupid gauge?

"Uhhh ... 85 pounds, sir," Woodie said, taking a wild stab at a number.

His guess was correct.

"You lucked out, Lieutenant," the Operations Officer said, barely suppressing a smile. As a pilot, he had an inkling of the probable background for the whole affair, but the charade of filling out investigation and report forms was necessary for the official record. He was merely completing his role.

"Now report back to the squadron, and don't bend any more airplanes," the officer admonished.

"Yes, sir," Woodie said. "Thank you, sir. I'll do my best."

Woodie breathed a sigh of relief and walked back to the ready room for his next assignment: ferrying a Corsair to San Diego.

The ill-fated OY-1 that was left in Missouri eventually wound up as a classroom reconstruction project at a small Midwestern college, where it served admirably in the school's aviation and flight instruction program. The purchase price from the Navy was one dollar.

Woodie would have been proud.

* * *

O'Toole, having completed the successful delivery of the OY-1 to San Diego, had returned to Columbus on NATS the previous evening. He spotted his comrade in arms in the ready room checking his Corsair assignment for the following day.

"How'd it go with the Operations Officer, ol' buddy?" O'Toole asked. "Chew you out pretty good, did he?"

"Naw," Woodie said. "It wasn't too bad when I told him about the oil pressure."

"What oil pressure?" O'Toole asked, knowing the real reason for the unauthorized stop in the wheat field. He was curious as to just what kind of yarn was now part of the official record.

"Well," Woodie said, "I simply told him about the oil pressure gauge showing a low reading and me feeling it prudent to land before I lost the engine. How was I to know the wheat was that high?"

The perfectly innocent look on Woodie's face as he repeated his explanation almost made O'Toole forget the story was complete fantasy.

O'Toole smiled in admiration. "It's a real pleasure to know a genius. I couldn't have done better myself," he said. "But we had better walk straight lines until it all blows over."

On their next Corsair ferry trip to San Diego, as they taxied into the parking area by the big concrete hangars that served as the West Coast terminus for ferry deliveries, the straight-as-an-arrow aces noticed an unusual-looking seaplane on the ramp.

"Aha!" O'Toole observed by radio, "There's an airplane I haven't flown in some time; it's an old Curtiss SO3C Seagull." A cruiser-borne scout observation plane, it was the very latest in scout planes during the early Thirties.

"I used to fly them when temporarily assigned to a squadron of Seagulls at Corpus Christi before being transferred to fighter training."

With the Corsairs tucked away in the hangar, the two Marine pilots examined the bulky float plane. Powered by an in-line Ranger engine of marginal horsepower, the SO3C was referred to by pilots assigned to fly it as the "gutless wonder." The consensus was that the engine just didn't seem to have the power necessary, considering the weight of the rather sturdily constructed airframe. The airplane's fuselage had a two-place cockpit with sliding canopies over the seats arranged in tandem position. Its wings were squared off and turned up at the tips, and a large center pontoon and two smaller wingtip floats seemed to have been tacked on. The structure was appropriately braced and held strongly in place by a complex of wires and turnbuckles.

In operation as the "eyes of the Fleet," the scout/observation aircraft was either launched from a catapult aboard ship or lowered over the side by a crane for a water takeoff. In calm seas, takeoff runs could be very lengthy, and very rough.

While Woodie signed in his Corsair at the Flight Office, O'Toole walked around the scout plane doing some nostalgic reminiscing. A voice behind him brought him to a halt.

"Did I hear that you checked out in these things, Lieutenant?" the San Diego FCLO asked.

"Yes, sir, sort of," O'Toole responded. "I logged about 50 hours in one at Corpus Christi, but it's been over a year ago. You need somebody to fly it some place?"

"Sure do," the FCLO said. "They want it up at Bremerton next week and we have to get it to them."

"How long has it been sitting here? And, does it run?" O'Toole knew the shortcomings of inverted, in-line engines. The oil invariably drained down into the bottom of the cylinders and fouled the plugs if the airplane wasn't flown very often, so he was understandably leery.

"Oh, sure," said the officer. "It's all ready to go. We can put it in the bay in the morning and you can fly it around a while to get the feel of it again, if you like. Then you can run it up the coast for us."

He's pretty eager, O'Toole thought, suspiciously. I'd better give it a good shakedown. Might be fun, though.

"Okay, I'll do it," O'Toole agreed. "You'll tell Operations in Columbus?"

"No problem," the FCLO said, unsuccessfully trying to conceal his relief at unloading what he considered his resident "lemon."

O'Toole ambled over to the Receiving Office where Woodie was signing off the Corsair he had just delivered. O'Toole proceeded to do the same for his ferry job, all the while mulling over in his mind his sightseeing trip up the West Coast.

"What's this about your going to Bremerton?" Woodie asked.

"Boy, news travels fast around here," O'Toole said. "I just thought I'd do it for old time's sake. It's not a bad old bird, considering."

"Well, I'm heading back to Columbus on NATS tonight, unless you need a copilot," Woodie said, wishfully.

O'Toole didn't see how he could clear that with the FCLO, so he wished Woodie well, then went back out to sit in the SO3C for a while to refamiliarize himself with all the cockpit gauges, switches, levers, and instruments, preparing for his checkout in the morning.

Noting that there had been no alterations in the cockpit and everything was pretty much as he remembered it from his Corpus Christi tour, he asked one of the linemen to stand by with a fire extinguisher so he could check out the powerplant. It started with

131

a puff of blue smoke on about the eighth revolution and seemed to run smoothly enough. As the engine reached operating temperature, O'Toole checked the magnetos. Both seemed okay. Satisfied that it would run for the seven or eight hours flying time to Bremerton, he shut it off and climbed down.

Stopping by the office, he picked up his orders from the FCLO, then went on to the Bachelor Officers' Mess for some nourishment. He decided to forego the usual social amenities of an evening at the Officers' Club and retired to the barracks to read the SO3C Operations Manual in preparation for the morrow's familiarization ride around the area before leaving for Bremerton.

The typical San Diego morning dawned with overcast skies and a ceiling of about 1,500 feet. Such conditions keep the area's temperature fairly stable, serving as a natural air conditioner. The relatively even water temperature warms the air in winter and cools it in the summer, making for a very short thermometer of 55 to 75 degrees. However, such 1,000 to 1,500-foot overcasts do not make for ideal flying conditions. It is possible to take off with the ceiling at the required 1,000 feet then to watch it drop capriciously to 500 feet.

O'Toole decided that since he was merely going to do a few takeoffs and landings with very little air work, the 8 a.m. ceiling, reported as 1,200 feet, was adequate. The line crew placed the airplane in the water and the pilot clambered aboard from his position on the wing. The linemen, grasping the various handholds, steadied the craft against the quay as O'Toole fired up.

The engine coughed twice and settled down to a steady idle, so he gave the thumbs-up signal for the dock crew to cast off.

The Seagull eased slowly out into the bay, away from hazards. The seaplane had no brakes or reverse gear. Afloat, a pilot is at the mercy of both wind and current, with only the propeller blast against the rudder and a passably effective water rudder mounted at the stern of the main float to maintain direction. Therefore, maneuvering sea-room was important.

O'Toole water-taxied out to the middle of the bay, throttled back to idle, and allowed the craft to weather cock into the mild five- or six-knot breeze, which was making a few ripples in the surface of the water. O'Toole knew that such ripples were all-important for a successful takeoff in this airplane.

Like all float planes, the pontoons of the SO3C had breaks or "steps" on the bottoms. When power was applied and speed built up, the aircraft could be made to rise on the surface by slight forward pressure on the control stick. If there were breaks in the surface of the water (ripples or waves), a slight tug on the stick would cause the release of the water's suction and the aircraft would become airborne. In calm waters, therefore, float planes, particularly low-powered models like the Seagull, could have problems taking off.

He retracted the water rudder, eased the throttle forward, and the SO3C began to pick up speed. He held the stick back, then eased it forward and felt the main float gradually come up on the step. At about 55 knots, he used a bit of backpressure momentarily and the aircraft broke free of the waves. It was flying.

The controls, though somewhat sluggish, were adequate and O'Toole banked around the bend in the bay at an altitude of about 500 feet. Headed south past Ballast Point jutting into the bay from Point Loma, O'Toole remembered reading somewhere that Ballast Point was so named because it was constructed of stones from Boston Harbor, stones used for ballast in the empty fur trading ships that visited San Diego 100 years earlier. To make the hazardous trip around Cape Horn at the southernmost tip of South America, the empty ships had to have adequate weight in their holds to keep the center of gravity low enough to prevent capsizing in the horrendous seas encountered while rounding the Horn.

133

These ballast stones were offloaded at the harbor entrance of San Diego so cargos of furs could be taken aboard. Over the several years such trade existed, this created a small peninsula subsequently further extended by dredgings from the bay and later developed into the submarine base that O'Toole flew by. As he climbed out of the bay, such musings were cut short in O'Toole's mind, and he applied himself to the job of refamiliarizing himself with the seaplane. He made a few turns, both at cruising speed and at slow speed, just above the stall, to see how much latitude he would have for landing.

Satisfying himself that he could handle the plane at approach speed, he headed back toward the bay to try a landing.

Holding the main float just off the water with some throttle, he touched the crest of a ripple with the step and cut the power, simultaneously pulling the stick all the way back.

The little seaplane settled gently onto the choppy bay, and quickly slowed to a stop.

With the engine idling, O'Toole headed toward the dock, remembering to reset the water rudder. He eased in upwind to avoid any weather-cocking effect on the rudder. The dock crew expertly made fast the lines securing the float as O'Toole shut down the engine and climbed out of the cockpit. He crossed the ramp to the Operations Office and filed a flight plan for Alameda, his first stop.

"How'd the checkout go?" the FCLO asked, guardedly.

"Seems to be okay," O'Toole replied. "I think it'll make it to Bremerton without falling apart."

His checkout had taken only a little over a half-hour, so just before 9 a.m., O'Toole tossed his green zippered bag into the back seat, slid open the front canopy, and stepped into the cockpit. The already-warm engine started easily and he soon was out in the bay, turning into the wind and smoothly opening the throttle.

After takeoff, he banked around to the left and out the bay entrance to Point Loma. Turning right around this southwesternmost tip of the United States, he headed up the coast to Los Angeles, the elderly Ranger engine maintaining a steady drone up front as the propeller sliced through the brisk morning air.

By then he could maintain about 1,500 feet without entering the overcast, so he merely followed the coastline to the Los Angeles basin. As he arrived there occasional breaks began to appear in the gray mist overhead.

Finding a good-sized hole over Huntington Beach, O'Toole eased the SO3C up through the dissipating cloud layer and continued on a northwesterly heading, which took him up over the Tehachapi Mountains and into the San Joaquin Valley. The usual headwind was not blowing so Bakersfield and Fresno soon passed beneath the wings, and he banked left at Modesto to begin the descent into Alameda, where the crew at the Alameda Naval Air Station dock promptly hustled about refueling the seaplane. A small crowd of interested observers soon gathered to see this strange airplane and ask questions:

"What did they use these things for?"

"Why is the engine installed upside down?"

"Why are the wing tips turned up?"

O'Toole answered them as best he could, reinforcing the explanations with some fiction of his own, while downing a sandwich and glass of milk, then filed for Bremerton.

After leaving the San Francisco Bay area, the Marine pilot edged east a bit and flew low up the Sacramento Valley toward Redding, California, passing west of that city on course to

135

Medford, Oregon. He checked his ground speed between those two cities and was elated to note that no headwind had developed, yet. The old floatplane was making a solid ground speed of 135 knots.

The weather was unusually clear as he approached the Pacific Northwest. Some of the worst weather experienced across the country has its beginnings here when the fronts cross the northwest corner of the United States and initiate their weekly forays southeasterly toward the Texas Panhandle.

On this day, however, the skies were clear and cold as O'Toole crossed over the Siskiyou Mountains into Oregon. As he was checking his map to ascertain the course to Portland, he noticed the round blue symbol of Crater Lake charted just off course to the east. He had never seen Crater Lake but had heard and read about this mysterious deep lake, created when an ancient mountain blew its top and the resulting crater filled with water, and impetuously he decided to take a close look at it.

Thanks to the lack of headwinds, O'Toole was running ahead of schedule, so he banked to the right and headed for the unusual geological landmark.

As he approached the lake from the southwest at about 3 p.m., the afternoon shadows from the rugged crags comprising the western edge of the lake were beginning to lengthen. The beauty of the clear deep water reflecting the sylvan surroundings was certainly one of the most breathtaking sights O'Toole had ever seen from aloft; he decided to descend into the crater for a closer look. Since the lake's area is some 20 square miles, the sightseer felt he should have no problem maneuvering the SO3C and routinely circled the lake at an altitude of ten feet inside the crater. But, when the time came to climb up over the rim of the crater and be on his way, the airplane simply could not gain the necessary altitude to go over the edge; the down-draft created by the prevailing wind rushing over the crater's west rim pushed the

aircraft down whenever it approached the rim, making escape seemingly impossible.

O'Toole realized he was in big trouble. Alone, off the airways, with no radio contact, his disappearance would remain a mystery hidden beneath the waves of the 2,000-foot-deep lake should the hull strike some hidden peak if he tried to land. He kept circling and thinking. Whatever had possessed him to come down in this crater anyway?

The fuel gauge showed about a quarter full, so the aircraft was fairly light. The wind which was causing the problem was out of the west, so he circled to the eastern side of the lake and coaxed the last foot of altitude from the laboring engine. Then he pointed the nose down and headed for the lowest gap in the western edge of the crater's mountainous rim. Skimming only a few feet above the waves, the throttle was open against the stop, the airplane's speed built agonizingly slowly to just over 155 knots. The trees on the crater's edge loomed increasingly large in the windshield.

At the last moment before plunging headlong into the towering fir trees, O'Toole reached over and pulled on full flaps.

The airplane ballooned up and over the crater's edge, then dropped precipitously down the outside slope. O'Toole managed to prevent a stall by nosing down and allowing the airplane to dive down the outer slope of the mountain until the airspeed once again built up sufficiently to level off and he was able to continue back to the airway to Portland.

His landing at the Naval Air Station at Bremerton was only a few minutes past his projected time of arrival. Splashing into the cool waters of Puget Sound at dusk, he taxied up to the seaplane landing ramp and shut down the engine. The linemen tied up the SO3C to the dock and O'Toole climbed down.

His knees were still somewhat wobbly from his recent harrowing experience. He just stood on the ramp for a few moments collecting his thoughts.

"You okay, sir?" one of the linemen asked.

"Yeah, I'm okay," O'Toole said. "Just kind of a long ride in this contraption. Where's the office?"

He entered the Line Office and signed off the airplane. Under "Remarks," he wrote, "Good airplane but somewhat under-powered."

Little red toy

As the massive Allied advance edged closer to the Empire, the Japanese use of suicidal Kamikaze tactics made it imperative that the U.S. Navy develop a new, realistic training technique for shipboard anti-aircraft gunners. The devastating damage sustained when the Japanese pilots flew their bomb-laden planes directly into our ships' superstructures had to be curtailed. The answer was to create a new type of practice target: the radio-controlled drone.

Naval materiel experts discovered that suitable target drone aircraft were available almost as "off-the-shelf" civilian sport aircraft and could be acquired inexpensively — by Government standards — thus making it practical for such target drones to be categorized as "expendable." In real life, it was soon found that they could usually be used for several training sessions. The realistic training of shooting at actual aircraft created such a heavy demand for the little drones throughout the Pacific Fleet training facilities that they became priority items included in the operations of the Ferry Command.

One of the small, 24-foot-wingspan, 150-horsepower drones was delivered to the Ferry Squadron in Columbus by a Culver Aircraft Company pilot so we could check out in it. That way, when the occasion demanded, we could go to Wichita and deliver the little planes to the Pacific Fleet. The cute little Culver looked like it would be a fun airplane to fly, so I managed to get my name on the list to check out in it and was issued a pilot's handbook to study.

The Culver TD2C was made in Wichita by a firm that had earlier marketed a small but fast wooden airplane known as the Culver "Cadet." A two-place aircraft, with side-by-side seating in an enclosed cockpit, and with retractable landing gear, it cruised at about 125 mph. This original design evolved into the radio--

141

controlled, single-place (for ferrying it required a real, live human being), retractable tricycle gear drone. This latter feature placed the third wheel ahead of the main gear rather than in the usual position at the tail. With such a configuration the airplane was much easier to handle on the ground, particularly at the high speeds and with gusty crosswinds encountered immediately after landing. During radio-controlled flight and subsequent landing, the tricycle gear virtually eliminated the tendency to ground-loop so prevalent in tailwheel aircraft.

The TD2C delivered at Columbus was, as were all drones, painted a bright vermilion, for optimum visibility during target practice. Their gaudy color soon rated them the nickname: "Red Bird." One bright April day, orders posted on the board said it was my turn to check out in the peanut-sized Kansas kiddy-car.

Having already read the Operations Manual several times, I grabbed my helmet, goggles, and parachute from the locker and hustled over to the hangar in which the diminutive plane was parked all by itself over by the huge hangar doors.

The Culver was Lilliputian compared to the Corsair. It would take some getting used to. A single lineman rolled it out by pulling on the propeller and I climbed aboard, wedging myself into the tight little cockpit, where a small bucket seat had been installed in the space soon to be filled with remote control electronic equipment.

Creature comforts were non-existent, but with the airplane's very limited range of 380 miles or so, one didn't have to sit in the cramped space for much more than two and a half hours at a time.

The tiny control stick between my knees seemed completely inadequate, but was reputed by my colleagues who had checked out already to be very positive in actual operation and to require a deft, delicate touch so as not to overcontrol. The rudder pedals were also connected to the nose wheel, which made taxiing as easy as driving a car. With the great visibility afforded by the tricycle gear level position and the plexiglass cockpit enclosure, movement on the ground was immeasurably simpler than in the Corsair, hence the Culver could be confidently taxiied much faster than tailwheel aircraft.

I hit the starter button and the little horizontally opposed, six-cylinder engine burst into life. Since I had no radio, the tower cleared me to the active runway with a green light and I released the brakes. With the engine throttled to a fast idle, the Red Bird accelerated rapidly and was soon rolling along the taxi strip at 50 mph, which was well beyond the officially prescribed limit of 25 mph.

Because of the small size of the airplane — my derriere was only a foot or so above the taxiway — I had the sensation of being in a racing car at high speed, and instinctively pulled the throttle back to slow idle and braked to a more comfortable pace. Actually, there was no real reason for my apprehension since I had complete control with brakes and rudder pedals. It was just that I was not accustomed to seeing the taxiway unreel that fast.

Poised at the end of the duty runway, I checked the magnetos, wiggled the ailerons, and received a green light from the tower for takeoff. When I pushed the throttle wide open, the little airplane accelerated to 70 mph but showed no willingness to fly at all. So I pulled it off with a tug on the stick; it became airborne and rose to perhaps ten feet, but showed no tendency to climb out of the ground effect cushion. With only 3,000 feet of runway remaining, I reached up and flipped the landing gear switch located in the middle of the panel. As the wheels came up, the rate of climb increased immediately. It occurred to me that this unusual takeoff characteristic was deliberately designed to accommodate the radio controls.

The unfeeling "black boxes" accomplished their work via distinct separate motions. Thus a sharp tug on the stick simulated the action of the radio-activated servo unit, and the airplane took off. This action was followed by the command to lift the gear, and the climb would begin. Ingenious engineering.

The propeller was a fixed-pitch wooden type that didn't afford the "gear-shifting" ability of the big Hamilton Standard constant-speed model on the Corsair.

With no low-pitch setting available, the maximum rpm obtainable on the TD2C was only about 2,300 at takeoff. However, at cruising speed — 140 mph — the rpm rose to 2,900. The pitch of such propellers must be a reasonable compromise providing sufficient power for takeoff and climb, but still not so low in pitch as to permit the engine to "run away" at cruise. The engineers had done their work well.

Slow flight produced no surprises as the stall was clean with ample warning before the nose dropped. Heading could be maintained easily with the rudder completely through the stall.

Satisfied that I would have no trouble delivering the drones 1,200 miles from Wichita to the West Coast, I reduced power and descended into the traffic pattern at Columbus.

Landing was uneventful, thanks to the tricycle landing gear, and I confidently turned off the runway and taxied to the ramp, letting the little plane roll along at about 40 mph all the way to the parking area. Unfortunately, my route took me right by the area overlooked by the office of the Squadron Commander, a regular Navy four-striper, Captain Arnold Sorensen.

As soon as I entered the Operations Office, the Duty Officer said, "You the guy flying the Red Bird?"

"Yes, why?" I asked.

"Skipper wants to see you — Pronto!"

Now what, I wondered, as I put away my parachute and walked down the hall to Captain Sorensen's office.

I knocked and a deep voice bid me enter.

The Navy captain was seated at his desk, his eyes — the coldest steel-blue eyes I had ever seen — boring holes through me. After I identified myself he asked, "Was that you, Mister, taxiing that Red Bird by the office a while ago?"

"I have just checked out in the TD2C, sir," I replied. "So, yes, I suppose it was."

"What, in your opinion, is a proper taxi speed around the ramp area?" he asked, with an edge to his voice.

"Certainly no higher speed than that where complete control cannot be maintained," I managed to reply.

"Just how fast were you going in that little monster, Mister?" He seemed about to explode.

"I don't know exactly, sir. The airspeed doesn't begin to register until about 40 mph or so."

"You were going like the proverbial bomb, Lieutenant!" the Captain roared, half standing, his fists knuckled down on the desktop.

He was now in full eruption. By using the word "Lieutenant" to address me, as opposed to the previous "Mister," he also was expressing an opinion of the Marine Corps in general as well as of me in particular.

"What earthly excuse do you have for so endangering the lives and property on this base in such an irresponsible manner?" he thundered, pounding the desk.

My face was by then a bright crimson. I managed to stammer, "Well, sir, as you know, the TD2C has a tricycle gear. Since I'm accustomed to the conventional gear of the Corsair, I suppose the ease of handling the drone by comparison tends to allow one to get carried away, and maybe the speed was a little high."

"A little high! Carried away, you say!" he said, angrily. "You keep that up, Mister, you will indeed be carried away – in a pine box! Let me assure you, sir, if I see you taxiing more than 25 miles an hour around the ramp again, I'll take serious disciplinary action. Do I make myself clear?"

"Yes, sir," I said. "My apologies, and it won't happen again."

Then, like the sun coming from behind a cloud, he smiled, stuck out his hand, and said, "I'm sure it won't." Then he grinned, "It is a fun airplane, isn't it?"

"Yes, sir. It sure is," I said, with a return grin.

The camaraderie of aviators had returned, and I was grateful for the gold wings on his tunic that made us members of the same fraternity. He remembered when he was a 23-year-old pilot, too.

About a week after my baptism into the world of tricycle-geared aircraft, the orders on the board in the Operations Office showed my name among the names of several pilots assigned to deliver six TD2C's to San Pedro Naval Air Station near Los Angeles.

We were to proceed to Wichita aboard the squadron's R4D transport, take delivery of the little drones, and fly them to California.

Mr. McDonald, our squadron's friendly airline pilot, loaded us aboard the R4D about 9 a.m. and we were off to the plains of Kansas. The flight took about five hours, so we decided to eat some of the dry cheese sandwiches provided for the trip. For the first time in my aviation career, I experienced a slight bout with motion sickness.

"S'matter, Marine? You look a little green around the gills," one of my Navy ferry group companions commented as I stretched out on the bucket seats to keep the sandwiches where they belonged.

"Your complexion is not exactly the picture of health at the moment either," was my feeble rejoinder.

I resolved never again to eat cheese sandwiches in an airplane.

We landed in Wichita at the airport used by the Boeing factory, then busily engaged in the manufacture of B-29 Super Fortresses. The whole ramp was filled with them, a truly staggering collection of bomb-delivering behemoths.

We spent the rest of the afternoon as the guests of factory personnel at the Culver facility, where we were conducted stop-by-stop along the production lines of the little drones. Our confidence in the TD2C was considerably enhanced by our first-hand observation of the craftsmanship used in their manufacture.

The next morning, after completing reams of paperwork officially accepting the little ships for the Navy, we were ready to go. One of the Navy pilots, Lieutenant (j.g.) Ian Swenson, was taxiing ahead of the rest of us out from the Culver Aircraft Company's delivery facility on the airport to the runway's center intersection. We had agreed that our tiny machines did not need to use the full two-mile length necessary for the huge Super Fortress.

When holding short at the center intersection, a slight hump in the airport surface made it impossible to see the end of the duty runway, and since we had no radio communication, arrange-

147

ments had been made for us to be cleared by signal light from the tower to taxi and for takeoff.

We were in a group of six, like a covey of quail, with Swenson in the lead. Having incorrectly assumed that the green light given us to taxi also gave us permission to take off, he had checked his engine's magnetos as he taxied out, and rolled out into the center of the runway headed into the wind. Busy with checking inside the cockpit, he remained blissfully unaware of the tower's red light frantically blinking the message to "Clear the runway!"

The rest of us heeded the light and remained on the taxi strip, all the while waving furiously to Swenson to get off the runway.

Looking up, he saw us and waved back at us, smiling broadly at what he thought were our fond farewells. Farewell was, indeed, almost precisely correct. A monstrous apparition in the form of a B-29 in the last phase of taking off appeared over the hump in the runway, bearing directly down on the hapless TD2C occupying the center less than a quarter-mile away.

The two pilots in the B-29's bulbous greenhouse-type cockpit suddenly saw the Culver and realized that it was impossible to stop in time to avoid overrunning the little red airplane directly in front of them. They did the only thing possible to avoid collision: As they passed in front of us, we could see both pilot and copilot horse back on the control wheels of the massive airplane, which miraculously rose about six feet off the runway surface, cleared the TD2C by inches, then slowly resettled to the runway.

Swenson's face was drained of all color as we taxied onto the runway and joined him. He turned and taxied mournfully back to meet the speeding automobile that was by then racing out to meet him. As we took off (with a green light, of course), we all shook our heads as we pondered just how long it would be before Swenson completed the pile of Incident Report forms facing him back at the Ramp Office. However, he was alive, and the TD2C was still in one piece.

Since the range of the little target drone was only three hours, it was necessary to stop between Wichita and Ft. Worth for fuel. The Naval Air Station at Norman, Oklahoma, was convenient.

Our flight leader, Lt. Roger Skellar, had matriculated at Norman in N2S Stearmans as an Aviation Cadet, so he was pleased to visit his alma mater. Of course, no one he used to know still remained there, since the Navy's population was highly mobile. But he still enjoyed telling us of his experiences while mastering the intricacies of flight the Navy way. Also, we were assured that Oklahoma City, the liberty town for personnel stationed at Norman, was most efficient at providing the necessary reprieve from the exacting demands of flight training.

One particularly amusing story Skellar related to us involved an idiosyncrasy of our cadet uniform. Our "dress whites," which were the standard summer liberty uniform for our weekend forays into town, included shoulder boards bearing a single gold star. While Skellar and a fellow cadet were strolling down a main thoroughfare of Oklahoma City hoping to engage in friendly liaison with some local femininity they were approached by a pair of buck privates from a nearby Army training base. As the distance between them narrowed to about ten yards, the Army lads nervously executed a perfect salute to the two Naval cadets. The salute was, of course, smartly returned. As the Army's finest moved, they thought, out of earshot, one was heard to remark to the other:

"I don't care if they are the same age we are. It says in the book one star is a general and we gotta salute 'em!"

The entire current class of Naval Aviation cadets swarmed out as we taxied in for fuel and plied us with a wide variety of questions about our unusual equipage. Sorry to say, most of our answers were calculated to set rumor mills in motion worldwide.

"Is this a new secret fighter, sir?" a lad would ask.

With a straight face, a ferry pilot would answer, "Oh, yes. These are the super-secret jobs that are going to attack Tokyo. They are going to be carried in special submarines."

"Will they really cruise at 300?" another cadet would inquire eagerly.

One of my colleagues, with all the solemnity of an aeronautical engineer, would reply, "Yes, although the water injection unit is only used in combat conditions to achieve the higher speeds."

The rumor mill continued unabated while our fuel supply was replenished. One enthralled youngster was informed that "The Australians were going to use them with trained kangaroos for pilots."

It was great sport, and we reluctantly departed Norman for Ft. Worth.

150

After takeoff, we maintained a nondescript formation at about 3,000 feet. The 160 nautical miles to the Texas cattle center required only about an hour and 15 minutes, so it was early afternoon when we arrived. The projected headwind that had made us decide against going directly to Big Spring, Texas, from Norman (300 miles) had not materialized, so Skellar decided we should press on.

Unlike Ft. Worth, Big Spring was a $3.00 stop, but we would be 240 miles farther along the next day. The little ships cruised at only about 140 mph, quite different from the 300 mph alleged by the cadets at Norman, so we needed to keep flying if we were to maintain our schedule.

Since our sole navigation instrument in the TD2C was a skittery magnetic compass, we simply followed Highway 80 west from Ft. Worth. This transcontinental artery leads directly to Big Spring, was convenient, and is reasonably straight.

Gradually, we tightened our loose formation up a bit and cruised along in a "vee" with Skellar in the lead and two other planes on either side of him. As we neared Big Spring, he eased the whole group down to about 300 feet, or less, above the highway as we neared Big Spring. The late afternoon sun was reflecting off the propeller disks as we skimmed over the Texas countryside just above the highway.

At cruising speed, the TD2C, like most airplanes, flies slightly tail high — or to put it another way, with its nose slightly down. To anyone observing the approach of the airplane from a head-on position on the ground, this gives the impression that the airplane is diving, hence that a collision with it is horrifyingly imminent.

As we whizzed along westbound, numerous automobiles headed east on the highway were seen to pull violently off the road and lurch to a stop, the occupants crouching behind folded arms, as we passed overhead. Glancing back, we could see car

151

doors pop open and the motorists making less than friendly gestures in our direction.

Such shenanigans were strictly against Navy regulations, but the sheer exhilaration of flight close to the ground at high speed caused such diversions from the rules, and all young military pilots were from time to time tempted to engage in this practice, sometimes known as "buzzing."

We made our presence known at the Army Air Base at Big Spring by circling the field in tight formation, and promptly received a green light from the tower.

Skellar signaled with his right upraised fist for us to assume a right echelon from which we peeled off smartly in succession, making what fighter pilots call a "break," then circled and, at ten-second intervals, landed one behind the other.

After parking our tiny charges on the ramp, we made arrangements for our RON at the Line Office and decided to go to the Officers' Club. We were again deluged with all sorts of questions about the minuscule drones, and the TD2C's performance capabilities were once more embellished all out of proportion to their design limits or intended application.

Since this Army Air Base was the P-47 Thunderbolt training facility from which our two "attackers" had come on my first Corsair delivery flight of a few months before, I was naturally eager to swap information with Jug pilots and compare thoughts about the identically engined fighters.

The opportunity presented itself that evening in the Officers' Mess and led to discussing the finer points of the two aircraft, including the reputed superiority of the "Jug" in overhead gunnery runs in which, as a planned combat maneuver, a high-altitude two-plane fighter section makes the run on an unsuspecting quarry far below. Since unalert pilots of the lower aircraft were usually unaware of their impending destruction, the overhead run tactic was consistently effective in actual combat. This technique was particularly deadly if executed out of the sun. We had heard rumors that Jugs often achieved a speed close to the terminal velocity of the aircraft.

During the discussion, in which all sorts of wild tales ensued, one of the neophyte Army pilots regaled us with his vivid recollection of an early morning mock overhead run he and his wingman had made on two unsuspecting Corsairs a few months back.

"We were practicing at 18 grand when we saw them tooling along at about 10,000 feet about a hundred yards apart. We peeled over and went right between 'em before they even knew we were around!" He obviously enjoyed retelling his tale of the one-sided encounter, when I interrupted quietly.

"The pilot of the lead Corsair on the ferry flight that morning was a Navy Ace who had just returned from the South Pacific and probably has more actual combat time than you have in the air. He elected not to mix it up with you two because our engines were not completely broken in and we had to deliver them in top shape for the guys doing the job in the Fleet."

The "Jug" pilot swallowed hard, then confined his comments to the design of the "Jug" itself.

Our aircraft, the Corsair, and the Republic Aviation Company's product, the P-47 Thunderbolt, shared the same 2,000-hp engine. The latter, however, had the new exhaust-driven turbo supercharger to maintain sea-level manifold pressure at high altitude rather than the two-stage, gear-driven type used in the Corsair installation. It was reputed to allow the Thunderbolt to operate higher than our aerial mounts, and the Army pilots used every opportunity to make us aware of this alleged superiority. The Jugs were heavier and less maneuverable than the Corsairs, however, so the Navy much preferred the latter machine for its scope of operations.

It was easy to see why the big fighter had earned its nickname, "Jug." The barrel-shaped fuselage with stubby elliptical wings and matching tail surfaces looked like a jug. The wide-spaced landing gear provided clearance for the four-bladed propeller when the belly of the fuselage just cleared the ground. Projecting from the top was a bubble canopy that looked as if someone had stood off and thrown it at the airplane, to which it stuck.

Like the Corsair, it may not have been a thing of beauty on the ground but was awesomely pleasing to the eye in flight, and its eight 50-caliber machine guns mounted in the wings made it a very effective lethal weapon, indeed.

Eventually the gabfest broke up. We finally reached the barracks about 11:30 p.m. Sleep came easily; it had been a full day.

The 6:30 a.m. call came right on time. After enjoying a huge breakfast in the Army Mess Hall, our quintet resumed its journey westward.

Taxiing out past the P-47's, we resembled a flock of baby chicks among mother hens. Some of the Jugs were warming up on the front line, and we were careful not to taxi directly astern as the propeller blast would launch us on a premature but brief flight. The big radial engines drowned completely the staccato sound of our 150-horsepower machines.

Flight Leader Skellar, having received permission for a line-abreast low pass from the control tower, took off first and we joined him for a sweep across the field at an altitude of ten feet, staying in tight to give the base personnel a good show for their hospitality. The Jug pilots waved enthusiastically as we skimmed past the flight line.

Because the weather due west to El Paso was said to be marginal for visual flight, we veered north to Lubbock, less than

100 miles away, to slide in behind the weather front, which was headed southeast through Texas, and to continue on westward. Incidentally, Skellar had some relatives in Lubbock whom he wanted to see, so we were soon landing at the Panhandle city's Army Air Corps Advanced Training Base, where we taxied smartly up to the fuel pumps to top off our tanks.

Apparently a couple of our group had taxied a little too smartly for the Operations Officer, an Army Air Corps first lieutenant. He soon arrived by Jeep in a cloud of dust at the parking area and proceeded to dress down the two miscreants as they disembarked from their mounts.

"Just what do you guys think this base is, the Indianapolis 500?" he snarled.

"No, sir," one pilot began. "This is a tricycle-geared airplane and —"

He was cut off by the lieutenant with, "I can see it's a tricycle-geared airplane, Mister," he snapped, "and from the way some of you people handle them you should be driving tricycles! Get in the Jeep. I am putting you both on report. I'm gonna teach you hot-shot Navy jockeys a thing or two about base discipline."

His blood pressure was against the stops and obviously he planned to make some sort of an example of the itinerant Naval pilots. Fortunately, the entire conversation had been overheard by Skellar, who had observed that his two Navy full lieutenant bars outranked the single silver bar of the Army lieutenant. Skellar strolled over as his two colleagues were dejectedly climbing into the Jeep.

"What seems to be the trouble, Lieutenant?" he asked, moving in close to the Jeep so that the two silver bars gleaming on his open shirt collar were clearly visible. The Army lieutenant began wondering just how his job authority as Operations Officer would stand against the additional silver bar of this Navy visitor whose charges had committed no really serious offense.

"Well, sir," he began, "they were taxiing much too fast and creating a hazardous condition. I simply can't permit that in the operations area."

"That's certainly understandable, Lieutenant," the flight leader said. "I wouldn't want any of my men to upset your routine here. I wonder if I could tag along with you in the Jeep with them and we can go over to your office and discuss the matter?" Skellar was wearing a tight-lipped smile with his coal-black eyes drilling right through the lieutenant.

"Certainly, sir," the latter said, somewhat lamely. "Hop in."

As they drove off, the remaining two of us saw that the tanks of all five TD2C's were topped off so we'd be ready to go as soon as the flap inside the office was settled. We hoped Skellar could pull it off.

"I wonder if I might use your phone, Lieutenant?" Skellar asked as soon as they entered the Operations Office.

"Of course, sir. Help yourself."

Skellar pulled a note from his shirt pocket and dialed a phone number from several showing on the memo paper.

It seems his relative in Lubbock was a high city official. The conversation was brief and cordial, ending with Skellar's invitation to "Come out to the base, and we can visit for a few minutes."

Replacing the phone in its cradle, Skellar said, "Thanks very much, Lieutenant. I haven't seen Uncle George for some time, and it will be great to reminisce with him for a few minutes before we take off for Deming. Now, where were we on this taxiing thing?"

"Well," the Army officer began, "we're just not accustomed to such speeds on the ground with these tail-draggers we have for trainers here, sir. It just didn't seem safe to me. After all, if one of your people wraps up an airplane here, it's automatically my responsibility as Operations Officer." He began backing off a bit.

"I can certainly appreciate that, Lieutenant," Skellar said amiably. "And I understand your concern for my men's safety. However, these airplanes are easily controlled on the ground at speeds up to 50 miles an hour so no real hazard was created.

"Did you get a good look at the little ships? They are quite a piece of machinery." Skellar was moving in on his flank by appealing to the lieutenant's fraternal instinct as a fellow airman.

"No, I didn't look too close," said the retreating Operations Officer, "but they seem to be well built. Why don't we have a cup of coffee while the line people fill the tanks, then I'll let you give me a cockpit checkout."

"What about Henry and Joe here? Are they still on report?" Skellar wanted the job nailed down.

"Well, now that I understand that no hazard was created, there's really no offense, I guess. Just hold it down a little when you taxi out, okay?"

He received prompt assurance that such would be the case, and all four proceeded to enjoy their coffee.

After the cockpit checkout and Skellar's visit with his uncle, we quickly bid farewell to Lubbock and, at 9:15 a.m., began the relatively long haul to Deming.

The prediction of the weather people was proving to be correct; the front had passed on through to the southeast and had provided us with a tailwind, so that we would make the 365 miles with a few minutes' reserve. I didn't like pushing it that close, but Skellar seemed to think we could make it. His assumption was correct, but just barely. We each landed with about three gallons of fuel remaining.

As soon as the planes were refueled, we were whisked off to the Army Air Base Mess Hall for lunch. As usual, we were answering questions about the little drones. Their small size and the nature of their mission again made them a subject of great interest to our fellow aviators at each base.

"You mean they actually fly these things by radio?"

What was to be commonplace in just a few short years was still in its infancy and the concept was hard to grasp.

"Yep. They will install the radio gear when we get them to the West Coast. Then the Fleet's anti-aircraft gunners will use them for target practice."

All pilots said that it seemed like a pity to shoot down such a pretty little ship, but concluded that *c'est la guerre.*

Soon we were off to Tucson, only about 200 miles away. Although our tailwind was no longer with us, we covered the distance in about an hour and a half. Lemmon Mountain just northeast of Tucson, at almost 9,200 feet, was capped with its winter mantle of white and was quite a pretty sight when we descended over Saguaro National Park, impressed by the size of these huge sentinels of the desert.

Skellar and my three other Culver colleagues elected to spend the night at Tucson but, since it was not quite 2 p.m. – we had picked up an hour as we crossed the time zone – I decided to push on alone to Yuma and refuel at the Army Air Base there and still have enough hours of daylight to continue on to March Air Base in Riverside, California. I was looking forward to spending the night visiting relatives and friends whom I hadn't seen since my college days four years previously.

With Skellar's blessing, I filed for Yuma, 225 miles west, and again the little airplane slanted up into the clear Arizona air.

Northwest of Tucson, the Army had constructed several auxiliary training fields from which students and their instructors sallied forth in North American AT-6's, known as SNJ's in the Navy — the same highly maneuverable, low-wing, retractable landing gear, two-place advanced trainer in which I had trained as a cadet. All branches of the military service used it for the necessary gunnery and fighter tactics training before transferring into the heavier combat aircraft. It was also, I was soon to discover, slightly faster than the TD2C.

As I passed one of the auxiliary fields at about 6,500 feet, I observed an AT-6 that seemed to be in trouble with its gear down; it was just barely hanging in the air. It never occurred to me that it might be an instructor teaching his student the airplane's slow-speed, gear down, stall characteristics.

As I crossed over the top of the trainer about 200 feet above it and dipped the wing out of the way to see what was going on, I saw two startled upturned faces.

All seemed well, so I continued on westward. However, it soon appeared the instructor, most likely an Army second lieutenant, resented my interrupting his student's learning process. About two miles distant, the AT-6 was on my tail and gaining on me.

I nudged the throttle forward to the stop and tweaked the mixture control for maximum power. Even with the nose down in a slight dive, the Culver could only indicate about 150 miles per hour, so it was soon overtaken, even though the irate instructor-pilot had forgotten to raise his landing gear. I only hoped he didn't have any ammunition in the single 30-caliber machine gun mounted ahead of the right side of the cockpit.

Since my aircraft was undoubtedly unfamiliar to him, he might attempt to subject it to its ultimate fate somewhat prematurely. It did, after all, appear to be an alien aircraft with its bright red paint job and its small size. However, he simply pulled alongside and I waved to him with my best smile showing through the canopy.

My wave was not returned; my smile was met with a baleful gaze encompassing all the official arrogance of a traffic cop noting one's license number as he ostentatiously copied the number of my airplane from its rudder. Then the AT-6 peeled off and returned to his base.

Since the drone had no radio, there was no means of making him aware of my honorable intentions in making the crossover. With qualms, I figured his phone call would precede me to Yuma. But wait!

He didn't know my destination was Yuma. But he could guess.

My mind was racing, trying to formulate the explanation I would give the Yuma FCLO for "creating a hazardous condition."

My mind gradually began to settle down as the distance from the Tucson area and the AT-6 increased while I began to concoct an alibi should the FCLO accost me when I arrived at Yuma. I would explain to him that the AT-6 was practicing low-speed maneuvers right in the middle of the Green Five Federal Airway, so I thought I would cross right over him as a gentle reminder to return to the proper practice area — sort of "putting the shoe on the other foot." He just might buy it.

Touching down at Yuma, I soon discovered there was no way to be inconspicuous in the Culver. The whole line crew gathered around as usual, plying me with all sorts of questions. This time, however, I countered with, "Yeah, guys, this is a super-secret job I've got to get to the West Coast today! Could you just top the tanks and get me out of here?"

160

I slipped furtively into the Flight Office and signed the log for the clerk on duty, scribbled off a flight plan to March Field, and eased back out to the TD2C. Quickly firing up the tiny airplane, I used its high-speed taxiing capabilities as much as I dared and soon reached the duty runway. Wiggling the ailerons for takeoff permission, I halfway expected to see a red light signaling me to return to the line, but mercifully the light was green! Throttle against the stop, I departed the premises and took up a heading to El Centro, all the while offering up little prayers of thanksgiving. The 195 miles to March Field, my final leg of a long, long day, began to fall behind me.

The shadows of the mountains through Banning Pass west of Palm Springs were getting long as I began the descent into the huge bomber base at March Field just south of Riverside. Taxiing up to the parking ramp among the monstrous machines based here, my little conveyance caused quite a stir among the linemen who came out in a Jeep to lead me to a parking space for my overnight stay.

Somewhere along the line the issue of refueling dropped between the cracks, although I assumed they would automatically fill the tanks before morning.

After seeing that the Culver was hangared for the night, I called my aunt in Riverside to announce my arrival. She and my cousins immediately came out and hauled me into their home, where I was soon reminiscing with them and several old friends from my days in school. Ultimately, I crawled beneath the sheets in the same bed in which I slept in their home while attending college. The next morning I capped off a most pleasant evening with a nostalgic visit to my alma mater on the way back to March Field.

After filing for the Naval Air Station at San Pedro and a quick walk-around inspection of the TD2C, I got into the cockpit, started the engine, and taxied out for takeoff. With a green light from the tower, I was soon on my way on the final leg of this trip.

Perhaps it was the exhilaration of the occasion that fostered a complete disregard for my fuel gauge during my preflight checks and while I loitered over Riverside observing the various landmarks of my early flight training there four years previously.

Finally, I headed for San Pedro Harbor, 40 miles west. The early morning fog had burned off, but the remaining haze made finding the short strip at the Naval Station a chore. Eventually, it jumped into view from the background and a green light from the tower invited me into the pattern. On downwind, I popped the gear down for landing.

Just as I turned crosswind, the engine coughed and began cutting out. Since my altitude was entirely adequate, I continued the approach and, as the aircraft flared on final, the engine ran smoothly once again and the landing was normal.

Only then did I glance at the fuel gauge; its unquivering needle indicated absolute zero. There was apparently only enough fuel in the fuel lines and carburetor to taxi to the parking area.

I rolled in alongside an amphibian, pulled the mixture to idle cutoff, and egressed, mentally castigating myself for not checking my fuel supply at March Field and for allowing my nostalgic, meandering visit over Riverside to affect my usually responsible preflight procedures, particularly using checklists.

The fuel lineman was calling me. "Sir, did you know this thing was plumb empty?" he asked.

"Oh?" I said, exuding aplomb. "Pretty good planning, eh?" And favored him with a condescending smile. It was the only reply I could think of. Strangely enough, he believed it.

I walked over to the Operations Office carrying my parachute and luggage, signed in the airplane, and stashed in my brain a resolution concerning fuel level checks.

Slightly used twins

In the late spring of 1945, the by then familiar manila official envelope in my squadron mailbox contained orders to Clinton, Oklahoma, along with several of my colleagues. I was to serve as a copilot for the delivery flight of a couple of Beechcraft SNB-2's then at the Clinton Naval Air Station to Corpus Christi, Texas.

This airplane, popularly known as the "Twin Beech" in its civilian version, was a twin-engine, executive transport with two vertical tail surfaces mounted on the ends of the stabilizer. Powered by two Pratt & Whitney radial engines of 450 horsepower each, it cruised at about 170 miles per hour and would outrun an R4D. The cabin accommodated up to nine people, including the pilot and copilot, so its uses in the Navy were many: twin-engine trainer, light cargo hauler, heavy admiral hauling, and general liaison.

Our squadron R4D delivered us to Clinton in just under six hours, arriving about two in the afternoon, local time, then continued on to Corpus Christi.

The SNB-2's to be delivered, we discovered, were run-out trainers destined for complete engine and airframe overhauls in Corpus Christi. They had been certified as "suitable for ferry flights only."

I suddenly realized that I was about to be introduced to another facet of the ferrying business; that of delivering "used" airplanes. I did not anticipate just how "used" they were to be, however,

When I first saw the battered, forlorn Twin to which we had been assigned, I was aghast. A small puddle of oil spread under each Pratt & Whitney engine, a sure indication that they had

165

several hundred hard hours on them. The airplane's cockpit seats were very shiny, with the upholstery considerably frayed around the edges and all power levers, control wheels, and rudder pedals were almost devoid of paint, worn off during the many hundreds of hours of training. The entire airplane appeared to have had no care or maintenance at all; with oil-streaked nacelles, cracked plexiglass, and faded numbers, it was really raunchy. With a little imagination one could hear a parade of instructors screaming invective at white-knuckled cadets learning the engine-out procedures on twin-engine airplanes.

Lt. Jerry Masters, for whom I would be serving as copilot, looked at the logbook of the time-expired Beechcraft and sighed.

"I'm glad it's not far to Corpus Christi." He added frankly, "I just reviewed the airplane's logbooks and have decided that the 'P&W' on the engines means 'pooped and weary'."

The weather the next day was marginal at Clinton, but was forecast to improve at Corpus Christi. We made careful preparations to be on our way south with the tired Twin.

Both engines started reluctantly, backfiring and surrounded by clouds of blue smoke, but seemed to run acceptably once the oil warmed. The magnetos checked okay, the props cycled, and when Masters ran them up to full power while completing his takeoff checklist, they took it in stride. The flaps worked, and the controls were rigged properly. At 160 miles per hour, the 550-mile hop to our destination on the Gulf of Mexico would take just under four hours. We didn't plan to attempt any speed records with those run-out engines. Rather, we would let them loaf along at about 1,800 rpm.

Air-cooled radial engines are marvelous pieces of machinery. They will take more abuse than the liquid-cooled in-line engines used concurrently in other aircraft. Their sole flaw is the large frontal area they present to the airstream. The radial's rugged durability and low weight-to-horsepower ratio, however, made them the number one choice of many aircraft designers.

When Masters lifted the worn-out airplane from the runway and I moved the gear lever to "up," the wheels retracted into the engine nacelles and, at 9:10 a.m., we were on our way.

We leveled at our initial cruising altitude of 1,500 feet just below the persistent overcast, headed toward Wichita Falls, Texas, and passed over the city about 35 minutes after takeoff. After some quick calculations, I informed Masters we were doing about 170 mph ground speed at the low cruise power setting.

"I figured on a tailwind," he said, nodding. "Maybe the old bus will hold together long enough to make it to Corpus at this rate."

A quick scan of the instrument panel indicated that all was well, so maybe this would be a nice trip after all.

Passing Wichita Falls, when we entered the East Texas hill country there was only a 500-foot clear area between the base of the clouds and tops of the rolling terrain.

Masters picked out Highway 281 south to Mineral Wells and eased down to about 500 feet above the road. The visibility below the cloud deck was good enough to see for ten miles, but the ceiling was lowering to only 200 feet above the sagebrush. Masters was driving the twin Beech like a high-speed automobile, at times less than a hundred feet above the concrete ribbon leading to Mineral Wells.

"Look at the sectional and tell me if there are any tunnels or high hills on this road," he said. His voice was steady but it was obvious he was not enjoying this kind of flying.

I ran my fingers along the highway shown on the map, and dutifully reported I couldn't see any unusual obstructions.

167

"See if you can raise Ft. Worth on the radio," he said. "If I can get a clearance, I'm going to go up on top of this stuff and run an approach to Meacham Field."

I reached for the microphone and set the transmitter knob on what was marked "Airways Frequency."

Ft. Worth didn't answer.

I tried another frequency. No response. The radio was as worn out as the airplane, and probably did not have any civilian cross-country frequency crystals in the transmitter. Its sole function had been landing and takeoff clearances at military training bases.

Masters shrugged as I gave him the negative information.

"Well, I guess we'll have to keep following the highway," he said. "I don't trust these old gyros for real instrument flying, anyway."

Indeed, the artificial horizon did not precisely indicate level flight; when the wings were parallel with the terrain below, it sat at least ten degrees off, certainly not reliable for safe operations.

The town of Jacksboro whipped past beneath the wings; it was only 27 miles north of Mineral Wells. However, eight miles south of Jacksboro, the road forked and the easterly fork led directly to Ft. Worth. Meacham Field was just to the left of this highway, only 45 miles away.

Since the overcast showed no sign of improving and a slight mist was developing, I asked Masters if he was going to stop at Ft. Worth. It was evident he was certainly extremely unhappy with our flight situation.

"Yeah, let's take that east fork and go on into Meacham Field and wait till this mess moves out of here," he said.

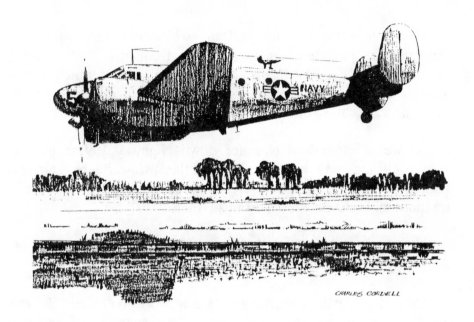

CHARLES CORWELL

"Now the only problem is to get through these mists for another 15 minutes."

Masters flew the airplane just to the right of the highway so he could see it as well as any obstructions that might appear, until it began to rain and water on the pitted windshield totally obscured our forward vision. Both of us were sitting bolt upright on our seats watching the highway unreel at almost three miles a minute, a speed which both of us realized could terminate our flight abruptly. At aircraft speeds there is simply no time to react should an obstacle appear. A pilot instinctively pulls up into the mist and goes immediately "on instruments."

Only by remaining a few feet above the highway, could we avoid entering the clouds, which would thus impose instrument flight upon us. The instant we lost sight of the ground, it would be necessary to pull up and away from the no longer visible terrain, and our lives would depend totally on instrument flight equipment we knew was untrustworthy, perhaps worthless.

However, once we did pull up, we would have to fly on instruments, including making a low-frequency radio range approach into Ft. Worth, probably without voice contact, and if another aircraft were making a legal instrument approach at the same time, a catastrophe was certainly possible.

So we continued to hammer down Highway 199 at treetop height all the way into Ft. Worth, the twin-ruddered aircraft rocketing by only a few feet above passing motorists below, undoubtedly scaring the wits out of them.

In a flash the town of Azle with its small airport passed off to the right. Thirteen miles to go.

"See if you can raise the tower now," Masters said. He was anticipating a respite from this aerial roller-coaster ride. I switched to the tower frequency and gave the tower a call. The response was immediate. We were informed that Meacham Field had a ragged 500-foot ceiling and visibility of one mile in light rain.

I advised we were already beneath the overcast and would be entering traffic from the northwest in three minutes. They acknowledged and cleared us to enter the traffic pattern.

In answer to our prayers, there was no other traffic, because of the weather. As soon as the airport beacon appeared through the smeared windshield, we dropped the wheels and Masters rolled them gently on the rain-swept asphalt, gauging his touchdown out the side window. As we taxied up to the Navy ramp, he reached over and pulled the worn mixture control knobs back. The big radials sputtered and klunk-klunked to a stop. The rain was making a steady staccato on the metal roof. Masters looked over and with a tired smile, grinned at me.

"How about a peanut butter and jelly sandwich, Mr. Copilot?" he asked.

"Sounds great," I replied. "And don't forget the carrot sticks."

So at just before 11 a.m., we unfastened our safety belts and, raising our inboard armrests, eased out of our seats and made our way back through the cabin, then made a run in the Texas downpour for the Operations Office. Although the distance was only about 50 yards, we were drenched by the time we entered. After closing our "visual" flight plan from Clinton, we proceeded to check the enroute weather farther south.

A clattering teletype machine was printing out the facts of the miserable conditions we had just flown through and was projecting the same for the Austin and San Antonio areas, so it appeared Ft. Worth might have two additional guests that evening.

The local weather personnel assured us that the situation was temporary and we should have good flying weather by afternoon to continue on to Corpus Christi. We had heard such optimistic opinions before, but conceded that anything was possible with southeastern Texas weather.

A pilot's ready room was adjacent to the weather and flight office areas of the Operations Building and, as usual, there was an excellent pool table to be used by ferry pilots to pass the time while waiting for the weather to improve.

While waiting, we munched on peanut butter and jelly sandwiches and kibitzed the current game of eight ball.

The foursome occupying the table were from the New York Ferry Squadron, on their way to San Diego with new Grumman FM's, the General Motors version of the F4F Wildcat. Although the stubby little fighter was being superseded by the larger, more powerful F6F Hellcat, it was still being delivered to offset losses at squadrons in the Pacific Fleet.

Eventually the eight ball dropped into the side pocket after a smooth shot by a Marine pool-hustler, Ben Adcock, with whom I had become acquainted during previous encounters along Green Five. He was quite good with a cue stick, so I was relieved when his partner and half the opposing pair excused themselves and relinquished their cues to me and Masters. Adcock aligned himself with me against Masters and the other player who was, like Masters, a Navy lieutenant.

The conversation around the table was most relaxing and the time passed quickly. By the time the two o'clock weather was announced, the rain had stopped and it appeared the fair weather trend was continuing all along our route to Corpus Christi. As it was only a little over two hours away, if we left before three o'clock we could make it before dark.

We filed for Corpus Christi and walked out to the twin Beech once again, sidestepping pools of water on the asphalt. Wet feet and a cold cockpit were not a very comfortable combination. By that time the sun was out most of the time, but scattered strato-cumulus clouds had prevented it from drying the puddles.

Masters lit off the radials and we splashed our way to the runway. The wind was still from the northwest, so we took off in that direction and bent the elderly twin Beech around to take up our southerly heading toward Waco and Austin.

As we went by Waco, the spelling of the name of this East Texas city reminded me of my early training in the Waco biplane, in which I learned the various aerobatic maneuvers three years previously. The memory was a pleasant one, and I shared it with Masters, explaining that there is no relationship between the city and the airplane, however. The name "Waco" is simply the initials of the Weaver Airplane Company.

"I've never flown one, but I hear they're pretty slippery," he said. "I learned loops and rolls in the Navy's N3N which, I believe, was beefier than the Army's Stearman." Then I told him about my outside loop in the N3N.

Masters smiled at my story but, as a multi-engine pilot, he was innately too conservative for such frivolity.

As we droned southward Masters and I reminisced a bit about the last time we had been at Corpus Christi. He, too, matriculated here — about six months before my class arrived — then had received advanced training in multi-engine transport category aircraft and was subsequently assigned to NATS, for a six-month tour after which came his assignment to the Ferry Squadron. We passed about 50 miles east of Austin, more or less following Highway 77 leading to Victoria, only 80 miles north of our destination.

The highway was an excellent navigational aid in the event that the visibility began to deteriorate as it had earlier. Soon, however, the city of Victoria was behind us; we called the Naval Air Station tower across the bay at Corpus Christi and were promptly cleared to land.

"Want to land this thing?" Masters asked, with a sly grin.

This seemed to be a nice gesture on his part; I wanted very much to see how this airplane acted as it quit flying. I nodded spiritedly and took in hand the control wheel on my side of the cockpit, and the throttles.

I went through the landing checklist, reduced power, lowered the landing gear, and turned onto final approach, holding an airspeed of 110 mph all the way down the glide slope.

I rounded out as we crossed the airport boundary indicating 95 and let the wheels touch at 75. I made no attempt to three-point the touchdown, as Masters had previously advised me to make a wheel landing, putting the main gear on first, then lowering the tail as the airspeed bled off during rollout, normal in this airplane. The mains touched the concrete with a slight bump and immediately bounced a couple of times as the big cabin-class twin began to porpoise.

Pushing the control wheel forward, I tried to hold the wheels on the runway as they contacted it again — and again. Up we went once more. Obviously, twin Beech wheel landings were not my forte.

After three such gyrations, I managed to hold the airplane on the runway, got on the brakes, and coaxed it to a stop, avoiding the characteristic ending of such gyrations: a groundloop.

Raising the flaps, I turned off at the last taxi-way. Masters was grinning broadly at my cheeks, which were red with embarrassment.

"Not everybody can practice three landings with only one approach," he said, doubling over at his own wit. "Congratulations!"

"Don't let it bother you," Masters said, wiping tears of laughter from his eyes. "Everybody who flies one of these things has the same problem for the first few landings. After a few times, you'll develop a feeling for it so you can hold the bouncing Beech down most of the time." He grinned again and chuckled.

I resolved to sharpen my skills with the twin Beech, with a good instructor.

As I taxied over to the hangar, we saw our squadron's R4D parked on the ramp. It had arrived earlier, to return us to Clinton for the second SNB-2.

It was past 5 p.m., so we arranged for a night's stay in the Transient Officers' Quarters, then made our way to the Mess Hall to catch up on some calories.

Arising early the following morning, we had a quick breakfast, then joined our R4D pilots from Columbus, McDonald, and Michael, in the squadron transport for the three-and-a-half-hour run back to Clinton to pick up the second SNB-2. We were pleased to observe that in twenty-four hours there was a vast difference in the weather along the route, a condition known to pilots as CAVU (ceiling and visibility unlimited).

We arrived at Clinton about noon and, shortly after lunch, preflighted the second run-out Beech. This delivery was made non-stop, overflying Ft. Worth, since the weather held all the way at somewhere between beautiful and superb. Looking down from 5,500 feet, we saw all the landmarks and terrain differences we had so dutifully used for navigational checkpoints between Wichita Falls and Ft. Worth the day before. Without the low ceiling and persistent drizzle splattering against the windshield, they stood out clearly miles ahead. Both Masters and I were struck by the beauty of the green East Texas hill country bathed in bright sunlight instead of driving rain. The easy ride over a mile above was a welcome change from feeling our way down that rain-soaked highway at 160 mph.

While easing down across the bay at Corpus Christi, Masters again relinquished the control wheel to me so I could redeem myself from the previous day's performance. I did much better, making only one bounce before the tail wheel remained on the runway.

"Ah, ha," Masters chortled, clapping his hands. "You're becoming an expert!"

"Sheer luck!" I grinned, ruefully. This airplane would take some getting used to before my landings improved to an acceptable level.

Again we returned to Columbus on the NATS R4D shuttle for our next assignment, arriving at our home base about one o'clock in the morning after a brief stop in St. Louis.

It was bitterly cold as we stepped out of the transport and when I finally crawled beneath the sheets, I was glad that the order board indicated I didn't have to report back to the squadron until noon the next day.

Midwestern Icebox

Spring arrived gradually in Columbus, with several false starts. Although there was a chill in the air most mornings, some days were almost warm, with the sun steadily inching its way northward once again as the vernal equinox in March had passed a month or so earlier. Fortunately, most of my deliveries continued to involve Corsairs to warm and sunny Southern California; consequently my stays in the frigid environs of home base were brief.

Deliveries along Green Five airway became so routine that my aeronautical charts were rarely removed from their case at my side in the cockpit. Personnel in various control towers and radio facilities along the way became very familiar, and I formed friendships with people I never saw but whose skills I respected and appreciated as each familiar voice came through the headphones in my helmet. Such vocal encounters made the time enroute pass pleasantly and quickly.

Under our squadron rules, if we made it to the West Coast and back in three days we had the day off. I did not take advantage of such alleged relief from cross-country flying because I always wanted to escape from the snow and ice of Ohio whenever possible.

However, this pleasant follow-the-sun routine was suddenly disrupted by orders sending me with a fellow ferry pilot − a Navy lieutenant (j.g.) named Pete Mathers − to Norfolk to deliver two Corsairs to the Quonset Point, Rhode Island, Naval Air Station. We had an opportunity to get acquainted during the three-hour R4D ride to Norfolk. He was from West Virginia and pointed out his hometown of Arlington as we cruised along at 3,000 feet. A soft-spoken, non-assertive individual with a wry sense of humor, he proved to be an excellent traveling companion.

After landing at Norfolk, we went immediately to the Officers' Mess for lunch. We were both wearing working khaki uniforms but had remembered to bring along our blouses, so we had no problems with Navy protocol. As always, the food was delicious and impeccably served. Then we hiked to the Flight Office and went through the paperwork to pick up our charges for the two-and-a-half-hour jaunt up the Atlantic Coastline to Quonset Point.

The base's meteorologists advised that flying weather was good for visual flight: clear and cold. Our destination airport was recovering from a recent blizzard, the weatherman said, but the snow had been removed from all runways and the field was operational; outside temperature 22 degrees.

Pete's antipathy for snow and ice may not have been as deeply rooted as mine, but we both winced and wished we had brought our overcoats.

The takeoff from Norfolk in the new Corsairs was routine and I joined up with Pete in a comfortably loose formation as we headed northeast past the Cape Charles Lighthouse. Navigation was no problem. We simply followed the beach past Atlantic City, then up Long Beach Island to Barnegat Lighthouse, where the shoreline bends slightly left, well to the west of the direct course to Rhode Island. If we took the straight shot, we would fly about 20 miles out to sea, and at 7,500 feet we would be hard-pressed to glide to the beach if our engines packed up. In late March, survival time in the icy waters of the Atlantic would be perhaps 20 minutes.

We could see the skyscrapers of Manhattan in the northwestern distance when Pete picked up his microphone and said, "That ocean looks a little cold for swimming. What do you say we ease in a little closer to New York and go up Long Island Sound instead of flying straight across."

Although both our engines were performing perfectly, I agreed completely. Besides, I always did want to see New York up close from the air.

Acting on his prudent suggestion, we banked toward the "Big Apple," crossed Long Island just east of Brooklyn, then headed east up Long Island Sound for Rhode Island, holding 7,500 feet to avoid the civilian traffic in the area.

Passing to the side of Montauk Light and Block Island, we entered Narragansett Bay at the Beaver Tail Lighthouse and began our descent to the Air Station at Quonset Point. Personnel at the station had cleared the snow and ice from the runway, true enough; but walls of white were packed so high on either side of both runways and taxi strips, that we needed guidance from the tower to find our way to the parking ramp. We felt like two mice in a maze following a piece of cheese on a string.

When I cracked the canopy and felt the blast of icy air, the thought ran through my mind that our forefathers must have been sturdy stock, indeed, to have survived such an atrocious climate!

For such a short hop it required minimum paperwork to deliver our Corsairs, then we made our way hastily to the Mess Hall to check out the base's famous New England cuisine at the evening meal. We were not disappointed. Steaming bowls of clam chowder — made with real clams — immediately removed the chill from our bones. Then came baked codfish with all the trimmings to confirm all we had heard about the gourmet quality of Quonset Naval Air Station's food. Piping hot coffee with fresh apple cobbler followed by an evening at the Officers' Club made this trip one to remember.

The day had been a full one, so we sought our sleeping quarters early. On the next day we would go over to Boston on the base's shuttle flight to catch a commercial flight back to Columbus.

The airline DC-3 deposited us back on Columbus soil a little before the following noon. Mathers and I walked into the Operations Office. I saw my name on the board and a note to see Lt. Masters, my twin Beech pilot of the month before. We were to proceed to Wichita forthwith, to pick up a new Beechcraft JRB and deliver it to Floyd Bennett Field in New York.

The JRB was the executive transport version of the SNB-2 trainer with which Masters and I had had our adventure earlier in the spring. Its interior was designed more as a working office than for mere transportation, with six beautifully upholstered seats and extra soundproofing to stifle the thunderous roar of the radial engines. Best of all, as far as we pilots were concerned, it was brand-new, unlike the dilapidated, run-out condition of the twin Beech trainers we had delivered for overhaul.

The squadron's R4D deposited us safely on the Beechcraft ramp at Wichita the next day in time for lunch. Then we were taken on a thorough tour of the manufacturing facilities where the JRB's and SNB's were born. To see aluminum, steel, and fabric come together to form a high-speed, comfortable aircraft is an enlightening experience.

Designers and aeronautical engineers who bring together relatively lightweight and somewhat fragile components of an aircraft to create an incredibly strong finished unit are truly geniuses. As we watched an outboard wing panel taking shape under the expert hands of the workers, for example, it was amazing to realize the ultralight aluminum ribs and spars would be supporting the enormous weight of the aircraft at speeds approaching 200 miles an hour.

When properly assembled, however, and sheathed in wraparound sheet aluminum firmly held together in the proper airfoil shape by a multitude of meticulously applied rivets, the whole affair becomes a marvelously efficient and enormously strong weight-lifting device.

After a refreshing night's sleep, we tossed our green zipper bags into the plush cabin of the new JRB, and slid into our seats up front. When Masters fired up the brand-new Pratt & Whitney engines, they sounded musical.

The enroute weather from Wichita to New York was reported to be suitable for visual flight until just west of Cincinnati, where a stationary front was accompanied by low ceilings and precipitation in freezing conditions. Columbus, only 100 miles away, was reporting a 3,000-foot overcast and light rain. After mulling it over, we decided to file for St. Louis, 400 miles up the pike, where we would land, refuel, eat, and take another look at the weather to the east. Our destination, Floyd Bennett Field, was forecasting scattered cumulus at 5,000 feet with five miles visibility for the whole day, so perhaps we could deliver the JRB with only one stop.

Masters and I were captivated by the gleaming array of new instruments and controls in the cockpit. During the run-up, he glanced over and smiled. "Quite a difference, huh?"

"Strictly first cabin," I agreed.

He fed in the power and the twin Wasp radials responded with a steady, deep-throated roar. The tail came up, then, at about 85 miles an hour, Masters lifted off the runway, banked to the east and climbed to 7,500 feet for the two-and-a-half-hour ride to St. Louis. Although the morning sun glared directly into our eyes, we cut the rays simply by lowering our airplane's sun visors and watched the plains of eastern Kansas pass beneath us and give way to the rolling hills of Missouri as we went by Ft. Scott. By the time the gray blob that was the smoke over St. Louis appeared over the horizon, a high thin overcast had diminished its rays to a feeble spot of light, making the landscape a mixture of nondescript shapes and drab colors with no outstanding features at all. The outside air was exactly 23 degrees. Spring had definitely not yet arrived in the Mississippi Valley.

The cockpit heater in our new chariot was performing perfectly, however, so the front office was snug and comfy when we descended into St. Louis.

Masters called for the wheels and flaps, then skillfully pasted the airplane onto the runway at Lambert Field. It had been raining earlier, and the asphalt taxiways still had little puddles here and there that spattered the underside of the new aluminum as we rolled up to the ramp and parked.

"Well, this is now a used airplane," Masters said, as he pulled the mixture to idle cutoff and the propellers spun down.

"Let's go get something to eat and check on that weather front over by Cincinnati," he said.

The front was still parked along a line extending down to Nashville from Chicago and showed no signs of moving. However, if we flew below the 6,000-foot overcast as far as Pittsburgh, we could make it to New York in comparatively clear weather, even though we would probably get our new airplane wet somewhere along the way.

Although it was almost 900 miles to New York, the forecast was for mostly tailwinds after we passed Cincinnati, so we filed direct. With the Beechcraft's seven-hour range − over 1,200 miles − we could be into Floyd Bennett Field at dusk, but the territory was familiar to Masters so we anticipated no problems. He personally saw to it that the tanks were topped off, and we departed St. Louis just after noon.

A check on our ground speed at Vandalia showed exactly 175 miles an hour.

"Moving right along," Masters said, as I handed him the computer and he read the figure.

We were cruising at 3,500 feet, under the overcast, encountering intermittent rain and sleet showers, each of which deposited a thin film of ice on the windshield. The ice melted quickly, however, as soon as we passed through the squall, and I breathed easier.

If it got no colder we shouldn't have any ice problems since the aircraft was equipped with the new wing de-icer boots and propeller de-icing alcohol jets. But a bout with sleet and freezing rain could still be a problem, for the boots would not handle that. I didn't like the idea of precipitation when the outside temperature fluctuated between freezing and about 40 degrees.

As required by Ferry Command regulations, we had filed a VFR (Visual Flight Rules) flight plan and it was therefore mandatory that we maintain visual reference to our surroundings. Even so, with the arrival of that ice on the windshield and when it began to rain harder, I was thankful that Masters was an accomplished instrument pilot, and that our airplane had the best equipment available.

Terre Haute was barely discernible through the precipitation off to our left as we passed over U.S. 41, that well-traveled escape route for winter-bound Chicagoans fleeing to the sunny beaches of Miami.

Ice formations were more frequent now, and occasional white opaqueness of the windshield made it necessary to "maintain VFR conditions" by observing the passing scenery out the side windows. The de-icing boots along the wing were pulsating steadily, keeping the wings free of ice; they were absolutely essential since a build-up of ice, particularly rough rime ice, not only created additional weight but also distorted the carefully configured airfoil section necessary to the production of lift. If ice grows thick enough to distort the airflow across the leading edge of the wing, the stalling speed could increase to such a degree that the airplane would simply quit flying, an event that would generate national headlines.

"See if you can get Indianapolis on the radio," Masters said grimly. We were now down to 1,500 feet to stay beneath the clouds.

"Tell them we'd like to change clearance to Columbus. I don't think we are going to be able to stay VFR much longer."

I tuned the new radios to Indianapolis and gave them a call. The response, from 50 miles away, was immediate. They gave us an update on the weather to the east and advised that Columbus was now 800 feet overcast with visibility two miles in light rain. The surface temperature was 34 degrees. Cincinnati was reporting about the same, except visibility was only one mile.

Masters pursed his lips, then elected to divert to Columbus; he also decided to file an instrument flight plan, no matter what the ferry rules said. Forward visibility was by then practically nil.

I obtained the necessary instrument flight clearance from Indianapolis air route traffic control center and we climbed into the overcast, continuing to our assigned altitude of 6,000 feet.

The temperature outside at that altitude was 26 degrees and rain and sleet slapped our windshield steadily, but not heavily. Ice on the windshield and our side windows had obscured vision so we were isolated in an aluminum cocoon sliding along the radio beam into Columbus. It was an eerie experience for me, for my flight experience to this point had not included any time in actual instrument conditions.

Masters, a superb instrument pilot, was actually flying the airplane himself rather than relying on the new automatic pilot.

As the few remaining minutes to Columbus ticked off on the panel clock, we were handed off to the controller at our home base. Masters made minor course corrections to maintain our position in the center of the beam. Any deviations from the course caused an immediate response in the earphones, since the Adcock Range System then in use consisted of four distinct radio paths leading to the station.

On either side of these paths (beams) were spaces designated as the "A" or "N" quadrants. The radio signal heard in each of these was a Morse Code "A" (dit-dah) if in the "A" quadrant or an "N" (dah-dit) if in the "N" quadrant. If one was on the beam, the two signals merged into one steady signal (dahhh-) and thus provided the pilot with reliable information as to his position. As the range station was approached, the signal became louder until directly over the station, at which time it ceased altogether momentarily. This "cone of silence" advised the pilot he had reached his destination, and he could begin his descent while following the beam outbound for a specified time. He then completed a 180-degree turn and followed the beam back to the station.

When he passed over the cone of silence a second time at the required altitude, he descended to the runway, which was aligned with the radio beam. If the runway was not observed when the airplane reached its minimum descent altitude, the pilot was required to execute a missed approach and try again or was directed elsewhere. The system was a good one, and was a credit to the ingenuity of those responsible for aviation safety.

We soon passed over the initial cone of silence and continued outbound on the beam for two minutes. Masters then turned 30 degrees to the right and executed a flawless six-minute procedure turn. This brought him back on the beam toward the station as he descended to approach altitude. The second cone of silence announced that we were on final approach. Masters asked for wheels and flaps.

As we descended through the swirling mist, he slid the left side window open so he could see when we broke out of the overcast. Our forward vision was zero through the thick coating of ice on the windshield.

I watched the altimeter unwind toward the published minimum altitude, below which we could not descend. I called the numbers to Masters, "300 feet to go."

We continued to descend.

"200 feet," I announced.

Masters was sliding down the invisible conduit with no deviations in course or attitude whatsoever. The man was a pro.

"I've got the runway," he said, as if he were giving me the time of day.

The throttles under his hand eased back as he planted the main gear on the numbers and lowered the tail. He did all this while maintaining his forward orientation by looking out the side of the airplane.

We taxied up the familiar ramp as I looked at the outside air temperature gauge. It showed 22 degrees. As we disembarked, the lineman casually walked up. "Looks like you've gone into the ice hauling business, sir," he said.

Masters and I looked at the exterior of the JRB. With the exception of the wing and tail leading edges where the de-icer boots had done their job, the airplane looked as if it had been in the freezing compartment of a large refrigerator. The ice had reached a thickness of two inches in some places.

"Better tow it into the hangar and let this stuff melt," Masters said to the lineman.

As we went toward Operations, my pilot looked at me, smiled, and said, "Welcome home to Columbus, Lieutenant."

"Thanks for the lesson," I said. "That's a little different from a Link trainer."

"That's for sure," he agreed.

Masters went into Operations and filled out the form with a reasonable explanation as to how we managed to wind up on the gauges in what was supposed to be a VFR flight. I was sure his report would be a brilliant piece of prose.

Two days passed before aviation weather improved from eastern Ohio and points east so that we could continue our delivery.

The sun broke out at last, we climbed aboard and set off about 10:30 a.m. on the final leg of our journey to New York. Since our estimated time enroute to Floyd Bennett was just under three hours, we were resigned to having a late lunch.

The weather was indeed no problem, as the early spring landscape of Pennsylvania slid swiftly beneath the wings of the JRB. As we approached the Hudson Valley and New York City area, the city's normal haze appeared on the horizon.

Visibility fell to less than five miles with the sun shimmering on the haze, but Masters knew the territory intimately and asked me to give Floyd Bennett tower a call. "Tell 'em we're 20 miles out and will be downwind in approximately seven minutes," he said.

The airspeed indicator showed that we were doing 180 miles an hour. With the nose down and no reduction in power setting, in cool air which was perfectly smooth, there was no turbulence to make the descent uncomfortable.

Masters was letting the Twin-Beech make up for lost time. I wondered if he was hungry. My own growling stomach was reminding me of how long it had been since breakfast.

Masters turned downwind just as I saw the airport. He hauled the throttles back and asked for the wheels and flaps.

"Want to do this one?" he asked, with an impish grin.

I nodded and took the wheel, then turned to final approach. I slowed it up to about 90 miles an hour and brought it over the fence. Holding it off, I let the airspeed bleed off and the mains touched at about 75 miles an hour.

Amazingly, they stayed on the runway. I lowered the tail wheel slowly to the asphalt.

Masters grinned broadly and chortled, "The airlines are looking for young men like you."

We taxied up to the receiving ramp and I pulled the mixture controls to the engines.

Welcome to New York.

Rather than going over to the Officers' Mess for lunch, Masters excused himself and headed for Connecticut. His hunger was not necessarily for food. He explained that he was born and reared in this end of the country, and that he had friends and relatives all over the place.

I wished him well as he boarded a cab for the ride over to the neighboring state.

"Say hello to your cousins for me," I shouted. He waved from the back of the cab.

"See you in Columbus," he shouted, as the cab sped away.

After lunch with a few pilots based at the station, I strolled over to the hangar to see some of the aircraft stored there awaiting delivery. I knew this to be the delivery point for the Grumman Aircraft factory at Bethpage, Long Island. It was rumored back in Columbus that fine organization had just evolved a new fighter, one even better than the F6F Hellcat, which was now going to the Fleet in large quantities.

This latest in the Grumman "Cat" family was designated the F8F Bearcat, and there in the corner of the hangar poised for delivery was one of the prototypes.

"You checked out in fighters, Lieutenant?" someone asked.

It was the local Ferry Control Liaison Officer, who said he needed a fighter pilot to deliver the F8F to Jacksonville, Florida, as soon as possible. My heartbeat doubled, then and there.

"Well, I've been flying Corsairs for a little over a year now," I said as casually as possible, "and I believe I've got the hang of it."

"Great," he said, enthusiastically. "Take this handbook and study it tonight, and you can take this thing off my hands tomorrow."

I accepted the book when he assured me he would reconcile this side trip with my superiors in Columbus.

Approaching the stubby little fighter, I noticed the similarity to its predecessor. It appeared to be a bit smaller, but with the same powerful Pratt & Whitney R-2800 radial.

The four-blade propeller was the most distinctive change. It did not have the bulbous hub of the Hamilton Standard. Rather, it was perfectly flat across the center of the four blades. The Aero Propeller Company had evolved this new design, which had proven to be excellent.

I climbed up the side of the fuselage, slid the hatch back, and settled myself in the comfortable seat to do some serious reading. If the FCLO thought I could fly this little monster, I would do my best to prove that I could. The cockpit was very similar to the Corsair and the Hellcat, so familiarization was easy, as I learned where each control and switch was located and practiced the blindfold checkout technique by closing my eyes and feeling for each. After about two hours of such self-instruction, their locations and shapes came automatically to hand, and I was convinced that I could fly the bird. I went over to the office to check out some charts for the trip to Jacksonville.

There was a tall Navy lieutenant standing at the office counter talking with the FCLO.

"Oh, there you are, Lieutenant," the FCLO said. "I was going to come out to the hangar and tell you. It seems Mr. Stanley here is already checked out in the F8F, so you won't have to take it to Jacksonville after all. I've arranged for your transportation back to Columbus in the morning."

So much for my afternoon's reading and fantasizing about my trip in the new Bearcat. I shook Stanley's hand, visited with him for a few minutes, and made my way to the Bachelor Officers' Quarters for some sleep.

The ride back to Columbus on the commercial airliner that I boarded at La Guardia in New York took exactly three hours. The west wind on the nose made our trip a bit longer than its eastbound counterpart, but it had one redeeming feature. It had blown the remains of the stalled front on up through New England and out to sea. The spring air was crisp and clear as the terrain below prepared to come alive once again.

In another month the grays and browns below would dissolve into the greens and yellows of early summer. There would be some late frosts and possibly some more snow as winter reluctantly released its icy grip on the countryside, but the worst was past. Our deliveries of Corsairs continued, with a few exceptions, in generally pleasant weather.

One such exception occurred in late April. The Corsair I was to take to San Diego had some unusual armament. Rather than the usual six 50-caliber machine guns mounted outboard of the propeller arc in the wings, this airplane had been outfitted with four 20-millimeter cannons. Apparently the two dozen or so of these modified Corsairs were to be used for the job of pre-invasion softening up of shore installations on strategic islands of the Western Pacific.

The heavy armament should be effective, but cannon shells in wing lockers could be a little touchy, if anti-aircraft fire smashed into the ammo boxes of explosive cannon shells, it might well ruin one's whole day at the beach. It was not likely that I would have that problem. My job was simply to get the airplane, sans ammunition, to San Diego as soon as possible.

The weather people advised against our usual route via St. Louis and Tulsa. They suggested an initial jog south through Nashville, and Jackson, Mississippi; thence westward through Shreveport and thereafter following Green Five, our usual route at Ft. Worth.

The object was to make an end run around the broad weather front moving through Tulsa and St. Louis. It was believed we could circumvent the disturbance by going around the southern end as it would probably swing northeast at St. Louis. We would make it to Jackson during the first half of the day and could go on to Ft. Worth in the afternoon. The prognostication was entirely logical, as the movements of these weekly fronts are almost as predictable as the rising sun.

Six of us, mounted in the heavily gunned Corsairs, departed Columbus at 9 a.m. and maintained an easy formation across Kentucky all the way to Nashville Municipal Airport, where we stopped for fuel. The 300-mile flight took just under two hours. We consumed the usual peanut butter and jelly sandwiches while the airplanes were refueled at the special Armed Forces ramp.

191

The weather front we were hoping to avoid was not behaving as anticipated. Winds at its southern tip were blowing at tree-bending velocities as they mixed with the warm air from the Gulf. According to the weather charts, our route south was still flyable, so we filed for Jackson and got off a little before noon.

The first 17 years of my life were spent near Chattanooga, Tennessee, and I wished to take a look at it from the air, so I parted company with my companions to make a brief detour.

This little sojourn to the left of the planned direct course to Jackson proved to be most fortunate. It consumed just enough extra time to put my arrival in Jackson a little after 2 p.m. In the meantime, my colleagues continued directly from Nashville to Jackson. They landed there about 1:35 p.m., refueled, and departed for Ft. Worth before the 2 p.m. weather sequence clattered across the teletype.

The south end of the front was now producing squalls of hurricane force around Shreveport. Three aircraft, an Army C-46 Curtiss cargo transport and two Navy F4F Wildcats out of Jacksonville for Ft. Worth, didn't make it.

The Corsair flight managed to land at Shreveport, where the aircraft were quickly pushed into a hangar and thus protected from the worst storm to hit the area in years. Howling winds and torrential rains continued the rest of the afternoon and into the night. It was after noon the next day before any flight activity could resume.

While they were hiding from the storm, I remained overnight in Jackson, which escaped most of the storm's intensity. When I departed for Ft. Worth about 1 p.m., I could see twisted trees and demolished buildings in the vicinity of Shreveport. My decision to visit Chattanooga the day before had been fortunate indeed.

Linemen at Ft. Worth swarmed around the unusual-looking Corsair as I pulled up to the ramp for fuel; the other cannon-equipped Corsairs had overflown the usual Texas stop and continued on to Midland, so personnel on the ground at Ft. Worth were getting their first look at the very newest in beach-busting ordnance.

After a relaxing night's sleep in the hotel downtown, I continued my westward trek with the airborne blunderbuss the next morning. With an early start and reasonable weather, I estimated that I could easily deliver my Corsair to San Diego by late afternoon.

El Paso and Coolidge, Arizona, personnel did their usual professional job of refueling promptly, so the mountains of eastern San Diego County slipped beneath the wings a full hour before sundown. When I landed and taxied in, the other cannon-equipped Corsairs were lined up neatly on the ramp; I pulled up alongside, folded the wings, shut down the engine, and slid the hatch open so I could walk over and touch the front cylinders of one of the earlier arrivals. They were still warm, so I was not late.

I stepped into the Operations Office as my squadron mates were completing the delivery forms.

"Hey, what happened to you?" one of them asked. "You missed some neat weather."

"Yeah," I said. "So I hear. And how were the crosswinds when you landed at Shreveport?"

"Oh, the hangars stayed in one place, so we had no problems."

The good-natured banter continued with only casual references about "those poor guys in the C-46 and F4F's."

Beneath all the kidding we all knew and accepted that we took serious risks on flights and that there might be times when our luck would run out, but we never dwelled on it. It was simply a wager with fate we were willing to make in exchange for the sheer joy of flight. There was no other explanation. Indeed, to a fellow pilot, no other explanation was necessary.

Adios via SNJ-6

A new crop of pilots had arrived at the squadron in Columbus when we returned from delivering the aerial artillery to San Diego. They were not the usual recent Flight School graduates this time; rather, they were veteran combat Marines returning from the South Pacific.

They were excellent pilots, accustomed to demanding and obtaining all the performance a Corsair could deliver. Most had trouble readjusting their *modus operandi* to the requirements of ferry flights. All resented having to be led as a "follow pilot" by an experienced ferry pilot. This, I suppose, was understandable since they had been doing their own navigating over islands in the South Pacific with occasional interruptions of 7.7-millimeter Japanese ammunition clattering on the armor plate behind their heads. To them, loafing around the dull civilian landscape of the U.S.A. was pretty tame.

Some soon discovered that navigation along civilian airways did require some attention to detail. A missed checkpoint here, a forgotten landmark there, and the terrain suddenly looks all the same. After a few emergency landings at small-town airstrips to pinpoint their location and the resulting mountain of Unauthorized Landing Report forms to be completed, they began to sharpen up.

Unfortunately, a few developed an insatiable appetite for aerobatics while overseas. Since the Corsair was an excellent aerobatic airplane, much cross-country boredom was relieved by performing slow rolls, snap rolls, and loops. They did not always make their fellow pilots aware of their intentions before engaging in such aerial antics.

It was about noon and I was tooling along at 8,500 feet about 50 miles south of Tulsa on the way to Ft. Worth. The weather was very pleasant with only a few scattered cumulus casting polka dot shadows on the Red River Valley.

A blue blur appeared in my left peripheral vision and crossed over the top of the cockpit so close I could see the face of the pilot in the other Corsair grinning down at me. I maintained my course and altitude exactly as he completed the barrel roll and joined up along my right wing tip. It was Oren Dobbins, one of the new pilots. Dobbins, a Texan, was living proof of the expression, "Never ask a man if he's from Texas. If he is, he'll tell you, and if he's not ... don't embarrass him by asking."

A voice crackled in my earphones. "Say, ain't that the Red River down there?"

I assured him that his observation was correct.

The river has for a number of years served as the boundary between Oklahoma and Texas. Most of the year it is merely an overgrown creek occupying the center of the broad pathway it has carved out for itself during its more rambunctious moments. Its channels had chewed into the red Oklahoma clay curves that meander across the face of the land in a series of 180-degree crooks and turns. Sometimes the riverbed places a pilot and his airplane over Oklahoma one moment and Texas the next within a span of four or five minutes.

On the first foray over a certain crook in the river that placed us officially over the sovereign territory of the Lone Star State, Dobbins breathed into his microphone to catch my attention.

"Smell that air," he exulted, "we're home!"

He immediately rolled to the right and disappeared from view as he did a "split-S" from his position off my right wingtip.

I rolled to the right and eased the throttle back. The airspeed built as I pulled back on the stick as soon as inverted and headed downward in a nearly vertical dive. Dobbins was just coming out of his dive at about 1,500 feet and as he brought the nose up, he did three rolls in succession as he picked up the heading for Ft. Worth.

"Do you always celebrate your return to Texas that way?" I asked. The question was purely rhetorical, as I was sure he did.

"Just thought I'd see how the range stock made it through the winter," he said.

Dobbins pulled in alongside with his wingtip just barely out of my propwash and we proceeded to Ft. Worth almost as one airplane. He was an excellent pilot, and was enjoying the heady experience of flight in a fast, highly maneuverable airplane.

We approached Meacham Field from the north and, as we passed over the airport, he was still in tight echelon position. I tapped my helmet, peeled off to the left, and popped the wheels. He continued on south for a few seconds to establish the proper landing interval and followed me in to land.

As there was no other traffic, the control tower tolerated the fighter plane approach and said nothing.

"These new Corsairs are really something," Dobbins said. "Not quite as fast as the ones we had in the islands, but you can really see out of the new canopy."

He was referring to the original "bird cage" type cockpit enclosure on the first models of the Corsair. It was made with a series of rectangular windows set in a metal framework that we opened and closed with an overhead lanyard. The first Corsair I had flown at Green Cove Springs had been of this type.

Visibility through the early canopy was indeed limited. But, because of its lower profile, the airplane was a few knots faster than the new models with the bubble canopy. Mercifully, the project engineers were finally convinced that an improved ability to see the enemy was more desirable than three or four knots extra airspeed.

Dobbins left the airport at Ft. Worth almost immediately, claiming he had urgent business downtown. He didn't give me her name.

My sleeping quarters were to be provided in the usual hotel. As always, the food was good and the bed was a welcome respite from the exertions of the day. Aerial acrobatics, because of the high "g" forces involved, could be fatiguing. My muscles reminded me of the liaison with Dobbins over the Texas/Oklahoma border.

Eight hours of sleep magically restored the resiliency of my muscular system and the trip to San Diego was completed the next day in routine fashion with no further encounters with cowboys from the South Pacific.

It was now the middle of May, and the whole countryside along Green Five was verdant with summer's colors. Even the arid southwest was not so drab as warm greens and browns replaced the cold grays of winter and spring.

As I signed off the Corsair in San Diego, the FCLO dropped a new set of orders on the counter before me.

"How long since you flew an SNJ?" he asked.

I tried to recall my last ride in the Navy's advanced trainer. It had to be an instrument practice session back in the previous December at Cherry Point — a whole year and a half.

"It's been a while," I said. "Why?"

"Well, here are your orders to go to Dallas and bring us a brand-new one from the factory," he replied. "Our squadron needs it for instrument checkouts for pilots going overseas."

North American Aviation, manufacturer of the SNJ, had an assembly plant in Dallas turning out the latest model, the SNJ-6, with all the latest radios and gadgetry. It should make an excellent vehicle for refreshing the techniques of pilots who had not been exposed to instrument flight since their cadet training days.

One never forgets these procedures, but skills become rusty, and there is very little margin for error when flying on instruments.

As the commercial airliner whisked me back to Dallas, I caught up on the latest progress of the war in the newspaper. V-E Day had occurred earlier in the month, and the country's entire effort was directed to the Pacific. Perhaps the war would be over soon, and the country could get back to normal.

What would be "normal?" The worldwide conflict had wrought many changes. What would I do with the remainder of my life?

Certainly there would be a surplus of pilots, so I probably wouldn't earn a livelihood in a cockpit. Even so, I'd like to keep my hand in aviation; it was in my blood now, like some incurable malady. The continual adventure of travel around the country was distinctly habit-forming and would be sorely missed.

The door to the cockpit of the airliner was open. I strolled up the aisle and stood just outside of the DC-3's front office, watching the captain and his copilot as they deftly plied their trade of moving people across the country at three miles a minute in solid comfort.

Rail passenger service was doomed. The tempo of the nation would be accelerated to the speeds so easily attained through the air. Aviation travel would be the norm rather than the slow, plodding pace of railroads. Indeed, it would be a repeat process of the era a century ago when the stagecoach and covered wagon were pushed into oblivion by the marvelous railroad system now crisscrossing the country. I wondered how long it would take for the transition to occur.

The captain's eye spotted me standing in the space by the baggage racks just aft of the cockpit. He invited me to join him and his colleague.

We conversed easily about our respective jobs, and he agreed that for cross-country travel, this was the only way to go.

"Some of the new four-engine jobs they are beginning to use now on the overseas routes are really something to see. The new Douglas DC-4 cruises around 200 and carries twice as many people as this one. We hope to have some before long for these domestic routes."

He was enthusiastic about his job and, since he was about twice my age, I was sure he would be among the first to be assigned to the new, bigger aircraft. Airline pilot seniority systems rigidly governed the pecking order of promotions. He should move right up the ladder. His copilot, a much younger man, would probably move over to the left seat of the aging DC-3 for a while, then his turn would come.

When the time for the slow descent into Dallas arrived, I returned to my seat and watched as the runway numbers appeared beneath the wings. My friend greased it in. The man was sharp at his trade.

Checking with the factory delivery personnel the next morning, I was told to report to the airport Operations Office to accept delivery of the new SNJ parked on the ramp with several others, and ready to go.

Since I had not sat in the cockpit of an SNJ for seventeen months, I requested a briefing from one of the factory pilots, who readily obliged me with a thorough checkout, paying particular attention to all of the new "navigational aids" installed in the airplane.

Even the smells of a new airplane are distinctive. The combination of aluminum, steel, plastic, wires, fabric, and paint along with gasoline and oil create an odor, indeed a fragrance, peculiar to each type of aircraft. Corsairs have their own unique smells. So do SNJ's. It is difficult to describe, but it is there, particularly when the airplanes are new.

My hands re-established the feel of the levers, knobs, and switches in their various locations, and I soon considered myself ready for takeoff.

As I walked through the ready room to pick up the SNJ's logbooks preparatory to my departure, I heard someone calling to me.

"Lieutenant, are you going to the West Coast?"

It was a young Army corporal who had a week's leave and he was going home to Oakland. He had already checked out a parachute, so I assured him he was welcome to come along with me as far as Southern California.

He smiled as he gathered up his gear, clearly relieved at finally catching a ride, particularly one that would take him most of his journey the first day.

I filed for Midland, our first gas stop, and we walked out to the new trainer, stowed our gear, and climbed aboard.

The later models of the SNJ had a unique starter system. An electric motor that turned a flywheel arrangement was actuated by a foot stirrup between the rudder pedals in the cockpit. The pedal was pushed down by the pilot's heel to start the motor and, after it reached maximum rpm (about ten seconds), the pilot pushed with his toes, rocking the pedal forward. This engaged a clutch that turned the engine's crankshaft, starting the engine via the stored momentum in the flywheel. This bit of engineering magic greatly reduced the drain on the aircraft battery and was an excellent performer.

The foot-operated inertia starter did its job and the engine lit off with its familiar deep-throated bellow, then settled down to idle rpm.

Taxiing was different from the Corsair. The visibility from the front cockpit seat was not obstructed by the long snout that gave the Corsair the nickname "Hosenose."

By looking out the side of his open canopy, my passenger could also see where we were going.

After running up the brand-new engine, I asked him on the intercom if he was all set to go. He nodded. I had checked his seatbelt and parachute straps before climbing into the front seat. Feeling somewhat like my friend the airline pilot the day before, I pushed the throttle up against the stop, and we departed "Big D."

As soon as the landing gear was up, I pulled the power and propeller controls back to a more conservative climb setting out of deference to the local populace's eardrums. The SNJ on takeoff unfortunately had the unsavory reputation of being the noisiest single-engine airplane in the Armed Forces.

As I banked toward the west, climbing to 8,500 feet, the feel for this airplane, in which I had over 100 hours, returned readily. It was an easy airplane to fly, smooth on the controls and quite maneuverable. It was also an excellent instrument training platform, being very stable with no unusual quirks to distract one from the details and concentration of instrument flight.

Cruising at about 160 miles an hour, we soon passed south of Ft. Worth and headed for Abilene. The air was perfectly smooth, and the outside temperature at this altitude was 30 degrees. However, the sun on the canopy made a very effective solar heater, and it was quite comfortable inside. My passenger appeared to be dozing in the back seat when I glanced in the rearview mirror above my head.

The two hours to Midland passed quickly. Soon I would have to try my skill at landing this machine. The wind was straight down the runway, so I planned a normal, three-point, full-stall landing.

It quit flying about 70 miles an hour and we rolled smoothly along the runway, slowing quickly to taxi speed. I remembered to unlock the tail wheel, turned off at the taxiway and rolled up to the parking ramp.

Had there been a crosswind, I would have made a wheel landing, which means flying the airplane right down to the ground until the main gear contacts the runway. The throttle is then closed and the tail wheel lowered to the surface, just as with the SNB. In this way, more positive control of the airplane is maintained and sudden gusts from the side are not such a problem. Such crosswinds can create a yawing motion at the moment of touchdown and cause the tailwheel to unlock from its straight-ahead landing position. The ensuing freedom of the full-swiveling wheel can result in some rather awesome maneuvers on the runway as the luckless pilot struggles — and sometimes loses the struggle — to maintain his heading with the rudder.

While our fuel tanks were being topped, I introduced my passenger to the time-honored ferry pilot luncheon of peanut butter and jelly sandwiches, plus carrot sticks and glasses of milk.

The weather westward seemed to be holding with only a few afternoon cumulus buildups around Tucson and Gila Bend. We soon mounted the new trainer again and were off to our next stop 560 miles west: Tucson, Arizona, about three hours away.

About 50 miles west of Midland, I watched as the unusual geological phenomenon just north of the town of Wink, Texas, once again appeared on the horizon. Its similarity to the sand deposits in the southeastern tip of California was the result of the same type of chemical metamorphosis in the soil caused by centuries of wind and rain on the local topography. Our airplane required about seven or eight minutes to traverse its 20-mile width.

We were about halfway across this God-forsaken portion of the West Texas landscape when, scanning the instrument panel, I noticed the oil pressure gauge was fluctuating wildly; it would show its normal 85-pound reading for a moment or two, then the needle would slowly move to 160! I stared at the offending instrument as the needle swung drunkenly back to 30 pounds, then returned to 85, hesitated for a moment, then proceeded to 160 again.

The forbidding terrain below did not offer an ideal spot for an emergency landing. The airport at Wink was at least 20 miles away. The SNJ glided a little better than the Corsair, but neither airplane was noted for its soaring qualities. If the oil pressure gauge was actually doing its job and displaying some malfunction in the engine rather than exhibiting a flaw of its own, we were in for a long walk through the sand. Our present altitude would not permit a deadstick glide to the airport. Aircraft engines don't operate long without the soothing bath of oil continually applied to the churning pistons.

As I watched the insane gyrations of the oil pressure gauge, it suddenly occurred to me that, since this was a training plane, the student's instrument panel was almost an exact copy of the one facing me. My long association with the Corsair and its single set of instruments had made me momentarily forget the marvelous redundancy of dual-cockpit trainers.

I picked the microphone from its receptacle and switched the frequency control to intercom. As nonchalantly as possible, I asked, "Corporal, look at the oil pressure gauge and tell me what it says. I always like to compare the reading up here with the one back there. It's the gauge in the lower right-hand side of the panel."

I watched him in the rearview mirror as his eyes finally fixed on the proper gauge. They were quite wide open as he fumbled for his microphone.

"It's showing 85 pounds, sir," he said. "Is everything okay, sir? Is the engine gonna quit?"

I assured him that everything was just fine, since I now realized it was the instrument itself which was the culprit, rather than the engine's oil system. The only adverse effect that could result was if the small line from the engine to the gauge actually ruptured a small leak could occur, but complete depletion of the oil supply would take a while. Miraculously, as soon as the western edge of the sand dunes disappeared beneath the wings, the renegade gauge settled back to a steady 85 pounds.

The episode had irretrievably marred my passenger's previous serenity, however. Continually, he scanned the instruments for any untoward movements or indications. Only when we were on the ground at Tucson did he relax. I explained to him how such malfunctions in new airplanes are a fairly common occurrence.

I made no attempt to explain why such deviations never seemed to happen over terrain suitable for an emergency landing. Whether such events were merely extensions of "Murphy's Law" or were preordained by Fate itself was a mystery I was not prepared to explore further with my passenger.

Leaving Tucson, we climbed to the northwest past the several Army Air Corps training fields interspersed among the broad stands of the saguaro cactus plants.

I recalled my encounter with the instructor and student in these same skies while delivering the TD2C target plane to San Pedro earlier in the spring. It would be interesting if such an event occurred now, since we were flying an identical aircraft (the Army designation was AT-6). I would like to see if the new model could outrun the older ones.

We did observe several flights of trainers in formation but remained well clear. My passenger seemed fascinated by all the aerial activity in the area. I explained to him that this area was where most of the Army's pilots were trained, since the weather and terrain were ideal nearly all year round.

Turning southwest at Gila Bend, we headed for Yuma on the final leg of our journey. The weather remained perfectly clear. As it began its downward plunge toward the Pacific horizon, the sun was now making visibility ahead difficult. My sunglasses provided relief from the glare, so we passed Yuma with eyeballs little the worse for the wear.

I called El Centro to check on the San Diego weather. The usual clouds were creating a solid overcast with bases of 1,500 to 2,000 feet, extending from the coastline inland to the mountains, so we would be detouring around to the north and through the pass at Beaumont and Banning west of Palm Springs. I could then proceed to San Diego under the overcast and complete my delivery on schedule.

My passenger was wondering what was happening as I turned northwest and we passed over the Salton Sea.

I explained the problem and told him I planned to let him off at Thermal so he could catch a flight to Alameda, and he was delighted.

We descended into the searing afternoon heat of the Imperial Valley desert and rolled up to the fuel pumps at Thermal.

While the SNJ's tanks were refilled, I walked over to Operations with my passenger and assisted him on his journey by introducing him to a TBF jockey who was leaving for Alameda momentarily.

The Turkey pilot was grateful for the company, and the corporal was overjoyed at his good fortune in making such connections.

"Just like the airlines, huh, Corporal?" I asked.

"Much better, sir," he said and grinned. "No waiting for tickets or anything."

We took off and proceeded in formation as we climbed northwest toward Palm Springs. I remained fairly close in off the big torpedo bomber's left wingtip until we reached 8,500 feet. Then I waved farewell and peeled off to proceed through the pass. He continued to climb and I watched as he disappeared to the east of Mt. San Gorgonio.

Mt. San Jacinto passed on my left with its snow-capped top glistening in the afternoon sun. The myriad colors created by the low angle of the sun's rays as I turned south were truly a beautiful sight.

March Field was off to the right as I began my descent to get under the coastal cloud bank as I entered San Diego County. By following Highway 395, the town of Escondido soon appeared and I knew I was 35 miles north of my destination.

The overcast was now down to about 1,500 feet, so I remained right on the deck. As I passed the Marine Air Depot at Miramar, I could see North Island looming across San Diego Bay.

My call to the Air Station tower was acknowledged forthwith.

"Roger, 126," I heard through the earphones. "Land on the mat, one ball."

The ball system of landing instruction was unique to San Diego's Air Station. It was a carryover from the old no-radio days when the base was known as Rockwell Field. A series of large balls were suspended from a pole by the hangar, and the number of them depicted the direction of landing traffic. There were no runways, as such, but merely a reasonably level mat of sod and gravel.

Since the prevailing wind was from the west, one ball was used to signify a westerly landing as it was easiest to raise only one of the balls on the pole. Only on those rare occasions when the wind was from the south would another ball have to be raised and the arrivals would land to the south. This procedure was retained as the field was improved and radios came into general use. The area between the runways was blacktopped and was still referred to as the "mat."

Single-engine fighters and trainers were always told to land on the mat, whereas transports and other multi-engine aircraft used the concrete runways. It created a sort of social "pecking order," with the rank of the pilot entering into the decision-making process at times. For example, if the skipper of a fighter squadron requested landing instructions, the tower personnel, recognizing his voice or plane number, would direct him to a runway, even though his aircraft might be an ancient SNJ he was using to get in his required four hours of flight time per month for flight pay purposes.

In my own case, a one ball on the mat landing permission was expected and graciously accepted. As this was my fourth landing today in this aircraft, I managed to three-point it in a reasonably acceptable fashion and taxied back toward the big concrete hangars on the north side of the field.

As I was turning into the parking area, a yellow towing tractor driven by a young lineman suddenly appeared from between two parked Corsairs. The tractor moved directly across my path.

I was rolling about 15 or 20 miles per hour, and instinctively stood on the brakes by pushing the tops of both rudder pedals, making the airplane's tail come off the ground. I snatched the throttle to the backstop on the quadrant by my left hand and simultaneously released the brakes so the tail dropped to the ground and I once again applied the brakes. The whirling propeller tips had missed striking the concrete apron by a fraction of an inch.

The youthful driver of the offending towing tractor looked back over his shoulder as he departed with his machine toward the hangar, his face revealing his realization that he was in big trouble.

I slammed the mixture to idle cutoff, set the parking brake, and leaped from the cockpit before the propeller stopped turning.

Grabbing my dangling parachute up under my arm, I raced to catch the culprit before he could park and mingle with his fellow linemen and thus remain anonymous. However, I was spared the necessity of chewing him out personally.

His leading chief had seen the whole thing. As the tow-tractor screeched to a halt in the hangar, he walked up and lifted the trembling driver bodily out of the seat with one powerful arm.

"What do you think you're doing, 'Boot,' driving an overgrown kiddie-car?" he erupted, shaking the terrified young seaman like a bulldog with a rag doll. He proceeded to administer a first-class dressing down to the hapless youngster, interspersed with appropriate salty figures of speech. I hadn't heard the likes of it since I cut out the Chief of Flight Operations on final approach to Kingsville one day as I was dropping a tow target.

My own anger gradually subsided and changed to a feeling of sympathy as the chief concluded his remarks by remanding the now thoroughly admonished lineman to the barracks for five days.

The chief turned to me, saluted, and asked, "You okay, sir?"

"Sure, Chief," I replied, "but weren't you a little hard on the kid?"

"Well, sir, it may have seemed a little rough, but these new boots we are getting in here now have about as much responsibility about 'em as a tomcat on Saturday night. If I don't lean on 'em pretty heavy, they think they can get away with murder. Besides, we need that new 'J' you just brought in, and we don't have time to change the engine and prop on it. How's it fly, anyway?"

"It's a great airplane," I said. "You might want to check out the oil pressure gauge in the front cockpit, though. It's giving some pretty erratic readings. But the one in the back reads okay, so I'm pretty sure it's just some junk in the line."

"Okay, sir," he said. "Put it on the yellow sheet and we'll look at it in the morning."

I walked back to the SNJ, retrieved my luggage, and proceeded to the Operations Office to sign off the airplane's delivery papers one more time. This day had been one for the book — pun intended.

Radar transition

Soon after the adventuresome delivery of the SNJ to San Diego, the Ferry Command segment of my aviation career came to an end. As usual, the orders for new duties were the result of an impersonal decision on the part of some distant adjutant who was required to supply a certain number of qualified pilots for a designated job.

While completing delivery of another Corsair to San Diego a few days later, I spotted a familiar-looking leather briefcase on the filing cabinet behind the counter in the Operations Office. It was my long-lost mapcase, the one I had left in the first Corsair I delivered six months before.

"One of the line mechanics found it and brought it in here," a yeoman behind the counter said. "We figured one of you guys would recognize it sooner or later." The yeoman apparently was accustomed to such misplaced gear and was pleased to return one more thing to its owner.

I was relieved to have the comparatively new maps back again as the ones I was using were becoming a bit dog-eared, but it suddenly became apparent that I wouldn't need them.

"Did you hear about the new orders for you Gyrenes at Columbus?" asked Howard Larson, one of the Navy pilots from our home base. As usual, the Navy gossip network brought all manner of rumors concerning orders.

I asked Larson which duty station was named in the orders and their effective date.

"Oh, I dunno about the exact date or place, but they are already cut. You guys are going to go to Pensacola or Jacksonville to instruct cadets, or something," he said offhandedly. I couldn't see how we could possibly be assigned instructor duty since the war was beginning to wind down and very few cadets were being trained any more. The orders probably covered "or something."

My return to Columbus on NATS was accomplished in routine fashion in typical midsummer weather.

Sleep, as usual, had not come easily while seated almost upright in the seat of the R4D. Although the seatbacks did recline slightly, the position was still not ideal for complete relaxation. I had just dozed off for a brief, fitful sleep when I felt the power reduction for the descent into Amarillo for fuel.

A glance at my watch showed it was not quite 11 p.m. local time. We had made good speed from San Diego.

The plane was lightly loaded. Most of the passengers got up and walked around in the clear night air of the Texas Panhandle. I remembered my first visit here back in January when the weather was different.

Sleep came easier when we were once again aboard and airborne to St. Louis. I barely remembered the stop. Nobody disembarked this time and only two new passengers came aboard. Lambert Field faded into the night as the drone of the big radials wafted us to slumber once again.

The wheels rolled on the runway at Columbus a little after 5 a.m. with the sun just beginning to start the day.

When I stopped by Operations to check in, I noticed a fat manila envelope in my mailbox, pulled it out, and dispelled the scuttlebutt about the nature of the new orders. They were to proceed to USMCAS, Cherry Point, North Carolina, for special duties involving flying.

"Special duties?" My mind raced, trying to decipher the term. Oh, well, we should see.

* * * * *

The journey by automobile to Cherry Point was an experience. The tires on my 1940 Ford were old and well worn, so I drove with the apprehensions of a fox traversing a cactus patch, avoiding as many bumps as possible and holding the speed below 50 miles an hour. The auto trip took three days, in contrast to three hours by Corsair.

After checking into my new quarters at Cherry Point, I reported at the Squadron Offices and inquired as to the exact description of my new "special duties involving flying."

"Oh, haven't you heard? You're assigned to the new GCA unit."

"What, pray tell me, is a GCA unit?" My curiosity was piqued.

"It's a new instrument landing system called Ground Controlled Approach using terminal control radar to direct planes to the runway in heavy weather. They've gotta have pilots to fly the problem to check out green crews in the radar trailers."

There. He had used the word "radar" twice right out loud for all to hear. So far, I had only heard it whispered in connection with vectoring directions for air combat. Now it apparently was to be a common device in peaceful use for preserving life rather than for its destruction.

I walked out to the ramp and opened the cockpit hatch of one of the parked Corsairs. Hefting my frame over the side, I settled into the seat and scanned the panel. My reflection in the glass coverings on the instruments stared back at me. I had indeed "lucked out." I was to complete my military service in my favorite airplane.

In all, I had delivered thirty aircraft during my six months in the Ferry Command — mostly Corsairs coast to coast — and had delivered other types to points all over the United States.

My contribution to my country's survival had been substantial, and I'd enjoyed every minute of my "duties involving flying." Best of all, it hadn't been necessary for me to kill a fellow human being, for which I am very grateful.